A N INTRODUCTION TO
MOLECULAR KINETIC THEORY

Selected Topics in Modern Chemistry

SERIES EDITORS

Professor Harry H. Sisler
University of Florida
Gainesville, Florida

Professor Calvin A. VanderWerf
Hope College
Holland, Michigan

Series Editors' Statement

ONE OF THE most important pillars of the theoretical structure of physical science is the theory of particles in motion, in terms of which it has been possible to interpret a large body of information concerning the behavior of matter in its various physical states. Basic to an understanding of virtually all areas of natural science, the molecular kinetic theory is an essential topic for our SELECTED TOPICS IN MODERN CHEMISTRY series.

We are fortunate indeed to have as the author of this important volume Professor Joel H. Hildebrand, who has for a half century given tremendous leadership in chemical education and research. Out of his experience as a chemistry lecturer, investigator, and writer, his rich background of understanding of physical chemistry, and stimulated by his vital interest in teaching, Professor Hildebrand has written this volume. We believe that student and teacher alike will find it to be stimulating and informative.

HARRY H. SISLER
CALVIN A. VANDERWERF

AN INTRODUCTION TO MOLECULAR KINETIC THEORY

JOEL H. HILDEBRAND

Professor of Chemistry, Emeritus
University of California
Berkeley, California

REINHOLD BOOK CORPORATION
A subsidiary of Chapman-Reinhold, Inc.
NEW YORK   AMSTERDAM   LONDON

TO THE TEACHER

NEARLY EVERY COURSE in high school chemistry or physics introduces students to the gas laws and to the application of Avogadro's rule to determine chemical formulas and atomic weights, and texts for college freshmen in both fields contain a chapter on kinetic theory. But a single chapter in a book that surveys a large field must necessarily omit many aspects of kinetic theory that are interesting and also assimilable by bright students.

There is growing recognition of the wide variations existing in student intellectual appetites and digestive capacities and of the appropriateness of affording them the freedom of choice of the cafeteria rather than the rigidity of the *table d'hôte*. Moreover, they often like to try the same fare cooked in different ways.

I trust that this treatment of kinetic theory will serve both purposes, filling the gap that exists between a single chapter and an advanced treatise.

I wish to express my thanks to my colleague, Dr. Berni J. Alder, for allowing me to use the photographs expressing the results he and Dr. Wainwright obtained by the method of "molecular dynamics" of the reactions of molecules in solids and liquids.

JOEL H. HILDEBRAND

May 25, 1963

55305

CONTENTS

AN INTRODUCTION TO
MOLECULAR KINETIC THEORY

TO THE STUDENT

THE WRITER of this little volume went through more than one course, in both school and college, which seemed to consist mainly of memorizing facts, transcribing from blackboard to notebook algebra that had very little physical meaning, and attacking problems by plugging numbers into formulas. Most of you have doubtless had similar feelings about some of your instruction.

The writer hopes that this book will appear to readers in a different light. It has the advantage, at the outset, of dealing with a subject that is probably playing a larger role in modern scientific thinking than any other. Everyone—whether scientist, engineer, or intelligent, educated nonscientist—interprets in terms of kinetic theory phenomena involving temperature, heat, melting and freezing, evaporation and boiling; it is basic to the design and operation of heat engines—whether steam, gasoline, jet, or rocket—refrigeration, and air conditioning. All professional persons concerned in any way with these phenomena need kinetic theory as part of their stock-in-trade. Furthermore, everyone needs some familiarity with kinetic theory in order to experience the satisfactions that come from feeling at home in his environment.

Our emphasis here is upon the concepts, rather than the formulas, of kinetic theory. These concepts are not definitions to be memorized; they are ideas to be assimilated until they become intuitive. To become really acquainted with them is like getting to know a person; you cannot truly know him from a photograph and a description, you have to see how he behaves in a variety of situations. In a similar way you may learn to predict with confidence how a gas will behave in a new situation. Many of the exercises at the ends of Chapters 2 and 3 call for qualitative answers, for example: which of two gases would you expect to have the higher conductivity for heat? As soon as you see clearly the several factors that enter into heat conductivity, you can answer such a question with confidence. As a matter of fact, we more often want qualitative comparisons than precise numerical answers.

Throughout this book we begin not by deriving a formula but by considering the factors that govern the phenomenon in question. We can answer many of our questions without being able to derive complete formulas. To do that would in many cases require some familiarity not only with calculus but also with thermodynamics. Some college freshmen, though not all, will have acquired some familiarity with calculus, but only the most rare exception will have studied thermodynamics. Still, you need not hesitate to use a relation that seems reasonable—reasonable even though you are not yet in a position to follow all the steps in its derivation, just as you can learn to drive an automobile that you could neither design nor construct. But try hard always to make any formula that you use "come alive" by having the symbols stand for concepts with which you have more than a mere speaking acquaintance.

It is fun to use the mind; it is dull to substitute numbers for letters in formulas that have little physical meaning.

It is wise to visualize each step in the solution of a problem. If it involves the final pressure upon mixing two gases at constant temperature, see in your mind's eye an appropriate arrangement of flasks and stopcocks in a thermostat.

Again, if you are not quite sure of the steps in solving a problem, write out each, as in the explanations in the text; your error may then come to light.

The book is to be regarded as a cafeteria, not a *table d'hôte*. It touches on more topics than the usual high school or freshman text in chemistry or physics. The author, in the course of a long life of teaching and research, had in his freshman classes at the University of California in Berkeley about 40,000 students. Most of them found chemistry, including some kinetic theory, to be interesting; a normal young person finds, like Robert Louis Stevenson's little boy, that "the world is so full of a number of things that I think we should all be as happy as kings." Nature has more fascination and "infinite variety" than Mark Antony saw in Cleopatra. The author hopes that you will find that part of nature here exhibited to be like Cleopatra in this respect and not like a dose of bitter medicine. At the same time, this book is intended only as an introduction. Many of you will eventually wish to delve far more deeply into the subject with the aid of mathematics, physics, chemistry, and thermodynamics. The author hopes that you will then find that this introduction gave you a good start.

Those who pursue the subject further will, in due course, study thermodynamics and more mathematics, and the author recommends to you the little book "An Introduction to the Kinetic Theory of Gases," by Sir James Jeans, published by the Cambridge (England) University Press in 1946. For those who wish eventually to master the subject, there is the monumental work by J. O. Hirschfelder, C. F. Curtiss and R. B. Bird, "Molecular Theory of Gases and Liquids," published by John Wiley & Sons, Inc., New York, in 1954.

A Note to Students Who Have Not Yet Studied Calculus

Occasionally, in the ensuing pages, relations will be expressed in the symbols of calculus. It is not necessary to have studied calculus in order to understand what these symbols mean.

Within the text there are statements about the rate at which one quantity varies with another, such as "the rate at which pressure diminishes with increasing height." Calculus provides the means for dealing successfully with variable rates. For illustration, let us think of a heavy stone dropped from the top of a tower 200 ft high, and ask what its velocity will be at the halfway point, 100 ft down. The total time for falling 200 ft would be 3.53 sec. The mean velocity of a moving body is the distance it travels divided by the time required, in this case 200/3.53 or 56.7 ft sec^{-1}. But the stone does not fall at constant speed; it takes 2.49 sec to fall the first 100 ft, only 1.07 sec for the next 100 ft. If there are marks on the wall at 10 ft intervals, and we have a good stopwatch, we would come nearer to calculating the speed at 100 ft by getting the time between the 120 and 80 ft marks; we would come still closer if we could get accurate times at the 110 and 90 ft marks. But an ordinary stopwatch operated by a thumb would not suffice to measure short time intervals with sufficient accuracy. If we designate the distance interval as Δl, and the time interval as Δt, then the smaller the Δ's can be made without sacrifice of accuracy, the more closely would $\Delta l / \Delta t$ approach the actual velocity of the stone as it passes the 100 ft mark. When these intervals become infinitesimally small, they are designated by the symbol d, and $dl/dt = U$, the true velocity at a point. Knowing, as we do, the relation that $l = \frac{1}{2}gt^2$, where g is the acceleration of gravity (32.17 ft sec^{-2}), we learn from calculus that $dl/dt = U = gt$ and $dU/dt = g$. The velocity of a falling body (unless air resistance is appreciable) increases uniformly with time at the *rate* of 32.17 ft sec^{-1}. In this case the true velocity of our stone at the 100 ft mark is 80.2 ft sec^{-1}.

If three variables are involved in a relation, as in $PV = RT$, and we wish to indicate the relation between two of them while a third is held constant, we write what is called a *par-*

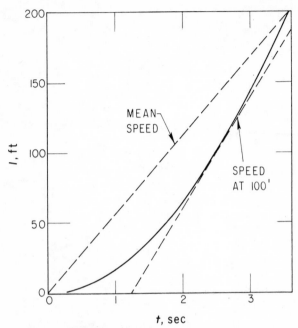

I, ft

t, sec

Illustration of the distinction between mean velocity over a range of
200 ft and the differential velocity at 100 ft, *dl/dt*.

tial differential. Boyle's law, for example, specifies the value
of $(\partial P/\partial V)_T$; Charles' law concerns $(\partial P/\partial T)_V$ or $(\partial V/\partial T)_P$.
The first of these is to be read simply as the rate at which the
pressure increases with temperature when the volume is held
constant.   Its numerical value could be expressed as atmospheres per degree.

THE DEVELOPMENT OF
THE CONCEPTS

GILBERT N. LEWIS, one of the great leaders in the development of physical science in the United States, wrote in 1923, "Science has its cathedrals, built by the efforts of a few architects and of many workers." Science is indeed an assemblage of great "cathedrals," most of them still under construction; it is not, as a certain dictionary asserted, merely "classified knowledge." Of all of its structures, one of the most beautiful and useful is Kinetic Theory. Its beauty, as the French physicist Henri Poincaré wrote, "is not that beauty which strikes the senses, . . . I mean that profounder beauty which comes from the harmonious order of the parts, and which a pure intelligence can grasp."

The adjective "pure" should discourage no reader. Anyone with enough curiosity to read this far surely has an intelligence sufficiently "pure" to permit him to see at least some of the main features of the structure of kinetic theory.

TWO LINES OF APPROACH

The reader may appreciate this great structure better if we begin by reviewing the process of construction, which, as with most cathedrals, extended over several centuries. Parts of it were at first built of poor materials which had to be discarded and replaced. Earlier "architects" worked along lines that seemed at first to have little in common; some were endeavoring to perfect a theory of heat, others to account for the properties of gases. Let us begin with the former.

The Nature of Heat

Francis Bacon (1561–1626) was on the right track at a very early date. He wrote:

> When I say of motion that it is the genus of which heat is a species, I would be understood to mean, not that heat generates motion or that motion generates heat (though both are true in certain cases) but that heat itself, its essence and quiddity, is motion and nothing else . . . . Heat is a motion of expansion, not uniformly of the whole body together, but in the smaller parts of it . . . .

But the few men who thought about such matters then and even during the following two centuries saw little or no reason to adopt Bacon's view, and another interpretation survived until about 1800. The scientists of the time imagined heat to be an imponderable substance called "caloric." Fourcroy, as late as 1800, wrote:

> Caloric penetrates all bodies; it separates their particles by lodging between them, and diminishes their attraction; it dilates bodies; it liquefies solids, and rarefies liquids to such a degree as to render them invisible, give them the form or air . . . . Hence it follows that liquids are combinations of solids with caloric, and that gases are solutions of different bodies in caloric, which of itself is the most attenuate, subtile, light and elastic of all natural substances; accordingly its weight cannot be estimated.
>
> All these facts prove that caloric is a particular substance, and not a modification of all substances, as some natural philosophers have imagined.

That Fourcroy could feel such confidence in "caloric" can be better appreciated by recalling that imponderable, subtle, penetrating substances were commonly assumed, at that time, in order to explain a variety of phenomena. Light consisted of vibrations in an elastic "ether"; combustible substances contained "phlogiston"; an electrified body contained an excess or a deficiency of an "electric fluid"; living organisms contained "vital spirits"; human beings differed from animals in having "souls."

"Caloric" dominated scientific thought until 1798, when it was rendered untenable by the historic experiments of Count Rumford. He observed the continuous evolution of heat during the boring of cannon that he was supervising. (Most persons do not observe and think earnestly about what they are doing.) He wrote:

The source of heat generated in these experiments appears evidently to be inexhaustible . . . . It is hardly necessary to add that anything which any insulated body, or system of bodies, can continue to furnish without limitation cannot possibly be a material substance; and it appeared to me to be extremely difficult, if not quite impossible, to form any distinct idea of anything capable of being excited and communicated in the manner the heat was excited and communicated in the experiments except it be MOTION.

This historic observation connected the concepts of heat and work. But "caloric," like the proverbial cat with its nine lives, died slowly, and became finally defunct only some half century later from a dose of experimental fact delivered by Joule. He measured the amount of water boiled off by heat generated by friction from a known amount of work. His result, 4.15×10^7 ergs cal^{-1}, was remarkably close to the modern, accepted value, 4.183 joules* cal^{-1} (1 joule is 10^7 ergs).

The Properties of Gases

The other approach to kinetic theory was through the study of the properties of gases. Evangelista Torricelli, in 1643, advanced the concept that we live in a deep sea of air, which

* Pronounced *jewel* by engineers, *jowl* by physicists and chemists.

has weight that presses upon us. He showed how a column of mercury can be used to measure this pressure. If a glass tube 80 or more centimeters in length is filled with mercury and inverted in a pool of mercury in such a way as to prevent any air from entering the tube, the mercury in the tube will sink to a height of about 76 cm (29.9 inches), depending on weather conditions and height above sea level, leaving a "Torricellian vacuum" in the top of the tube. (This space contains mercury vapor at extremely low pressure.) The height of the mercury column above the surface of the mercury in the trough just balances the pressure of the air. The apparatus depicted in principle in Fig. 1.1 thus serves as a *barometer* (from the Greek *baros*, weight, + *meter*). A height of 76.00 cm (760 mm) of mercury is taken as the *standard* atmosphere. Since 1 cm^3 of mercury at 0°C weighs 13.596 g the

Fig. 1.1 Mercury barometer
(schematic representation).
The scale is adjusted by means of a rack and pinion so that the point just touches the surface of the mercury in the trough.

standard atmosphere is equal to the gravitational force exerted on unit area by $13.596 \times 76.00 = 1.0333 \times 10^3$ g of mercury at sea level, which is 1.0333×10^3 g $\times$ 980.62 cm sec^{-2} $\times$ 1 cm^{-2} = 1.0133×10^6 dynes cm^{-2}. In English units the standard atmosphere may be shown to be equal to 14.7 pounds per square inch.

The pressure of gas in any container can be measured by the height of a column of mercury it will support, which thus serves as a *manometer*, or general measure of gas pressure.

Boyle's Law. About 1680, Robert Boyle measured the volumes of a fixed quantity of gas at different pressures (with constant temperature). Table 1.1 gives some of his actual figures. The product, PV, is practically constant; the fluctuations can be accounted for by the imprecision of his measurements of P and V. This important relation is known as *Boyle's law.* An equivalent statement is that at constant temperature P and V are inversely proportional.

TABLE 1.1   Boyle's Figures for PV

Volume (V)	Pressure (P)	Product (PV)
48.0	1.00	48.0
38.0	1.27	48.3
23.0	2.10	48.3
13.0	3.70	48.1

Boyle himself suggested two alternative hypotheses to account for this relation: that air consists of (1) particles at rest which repel each other or (2) particles in violent motion within a turbulent subtle fluid, which, one can see, suggests "caloric."

Newton showed mathematically that Boyle's law would follow from the assumption of a repulsive force between static particles varying inversely with the first power of the distance between them, but he recognized a serious weakness in such a hypothesis in that gas pressure would then depend upon the shape of the vessel.

To assert that the particles of gases repel one another, whereas those of liquids and solids attract, did not seem as inconsistent to men of the time as it really is, because the gases that were the subjects of their experiments had resisted all attempts to liquefy them by subjecting them to high pressures, and they were called "permanent gases." A developed kinetic theory was required in order to reveal the fact that the key to their liquefaction is low temperature, far lower than any then obtainable by freezing mixtures of ice and salt.

The scientists of the day were so deeply steeped in the "caloric fluid" that although Daniel Bernoulli, in 1738, had published a qualitative statement of gas kinetic theory, a century elapsed before the concept was seriously considered.

Charles' Law. An important relation was discovered toward the end of the century independently by Joseph Louis Gay-Lussac and by Jacques Charles, namely, that the pressure of a gas held at constant volume increases linearly with temperature. The increase amounts almost exactly to 1/273 of the pressure at 0° C per degree rise in temperature. It follows from Boyle's law that if the pressure of a fixed amount of gas is kept constant the volume of the gas will increase at the rate of 1/273 per degree.

Boyle's law may be represented graphically in either of the two ways, one as shown in Fig. 1.2, the other, a plot of *PV* vs. *P*. Charles' law is represented in Fig. 1.3 for two different initial pressures and volumes of the same amount of gas. As the temperature is lowered, the pressure decreases linearly until the gas condenses to liquid. All the lines cut the horizontal axis at −273° C. It is obviously logical to designate this point as the zero point of an "absolute" scale, now generally designated as the *Kelvin scale* of temperature. It is customary to denote temperatures on the centigrade scale by *t*,

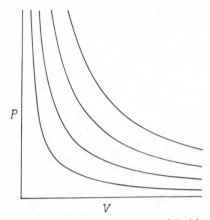

Fig. 1.2 Graphic representation of Boyle's law for various amounts of gas or different temperatures.

and on the Kelvin scale by T. Engineers in England and the United States often use a "Rankine" scale, with Fahrenheit

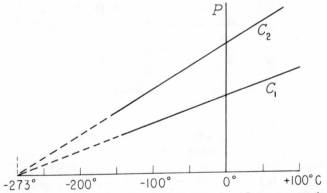

Fig. 1.3 Graphic representation of Charles' law for different concentrations of gas.

degrees. The relation between these scales is illustrated in Fig. 1.4.

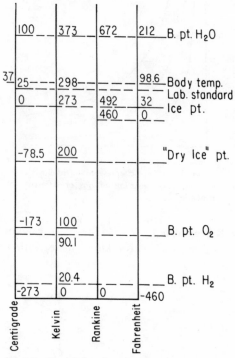

Centigrade	Kelvin	Rankine	Fahrenheit	
100	373	672	212	B. pt. H₂O
37 25	298		98.6	Body temp. Lab. standard
0	273	492 460	32 0	Ice pt.
-78.5	200			"Dry Ice" pt.
-173	100 90.1			B. pt. O₂
-273	20.4 0	0	-460	B. pt. H₂

Fig. 1.4 The relation between different temperature scales.

Charles' law can now be stated very simply: the pressure of a fixed amount and volume of gas varies directly with its absolute (Kelvin) temperature, that is: $P \propto T$, or P/T is constant. If P is kept constant, then, since PV is constant, V/T is constant.

Charles' and Boyle's laws can be combined into one expression by means of simple reasoning. Let us make it quite clear by using definite numbers, in order to aid in deciding whether a change in one variable increases or decreases another. Let us ask, what will be the final pressure if 10 liters of air at 0° C and a pressure of 20 cm of mercury is first compressed to 9 liters at 0° C and then heated to 25° C? To compress the gas to 9/10 of its volume requires *increasing* the pressure to 10/9 of its initial value, or 20 × 10/9 cm. Next, keeping the volume at 9 liters, the temperature is raised from 0 to 25° C, which is from 273 to 298° K. This further increases the pressure to

$$(298/273) \times (10/9) \times 20 = 24.3 \text{ cm}$$

If we collect the initial values on the left of the equation and the final values on the right, we obtain:

$$(20 \times 10)/273 = (24.3 \times 9)/298 = 0.734$$

We would have obtained the same result by changing temperature first, and volume second. (Try it!)

All problems of this sort can be solved stepwise in this way by logic that is little more than common sense. Now, common sense is more reliable than memory, and to apply simple, logical analysis to a problem like the above is safer than to try to remember a formula. Of course, if many such problems are to be solved, the logic can be crystallized into a formula, in order to save thinking through each case. To express the above logic in a formula we designate the initial values by P, V, and T and the final values by P', V', and T', whence $PV/T = P'V'/T' = $ constant. The magnitude of the constant depends upon the amount of gas. If the quantity is 1 mole, the value of V is nearly the same for all gases at $T = 273.16°$ K and 1 atm (see Table 2.1). Taking $V = 22.412$ liters, $PV/T = 0.08206$ liter atm mole^{-1} deg^{-1}. This is the gas law constant, commonly designated by R. If V is expressed in cubic centimeters then $R = 82.06$ cm^3 atm mole^{-1} deg^{-1}.

If pressure is expressed in millimeters of mercury, these numbers must be multiplied by 760. It is essential to use the numerical value of R which corresponds to the units used for P and V. It is often desirable to express R in calories per degree. Since 1 atm = 1.0133×10^6 dynes cm^{-2}, 82.06 cm^3 atm mole^{-1} deg^{-1} = 83.09×10^6 ergs mole^{-1} deg^{-1} = 8.309 joules mole^{-1} deg^{-1}; and since 1 cal = 4.183 joules, R = 1.985 cal mole^{-1} deg^{-1}. These values are listed in Table 1.2 for ready reference.

TABLE 1.2   Values of the Gas Constant (R) in Different Units

82.06	cm^3 atm deg^{-1} mole^{-1}
0.08206	liter atm deg^{-1} mole^{-1}
83.09×10^6	erg deg^{-1} mole^{-1}
8.309	joule deg^{-1} mole^{-1}
1.986	cal deg^{-1} mole^{-1}

chapter two ───────────────────────────

THE IDEAL OR PERFECT GAS

The Basic Concept

THE STATEMENT OF the kinetic theory made by Bernouilli in 1738 appeared in a publication little known to a public not ready to accept it, and over a century passed before its successful launching in 1856, by August Krönig,[*] a German schoolmaster, and independently a year later by Rudolf Julius Clausius,[†] a professor of physics.

The basic concept can be simply stated and easily visualized. A gas at moderate pressures consists of molecules flying about in random fashion, colliding elastically with each other and with the walls of the container. The total intrinsic volume of the molecules is so much smaller than the volume of the container as to be practically negligible as a first approximation.

The volumes occupied by 1 mole of all gases at $0°C$ and 1 atm pressure do not vary much from 22,400 cm^3, as illustrated in Table 2.1. The actual volume of the molecules themselves is only a tiny fraction of the volume they occupy as gas. A mole of hydrogen molecules, closely packed as they are in the solid state at $10°K$, occupies only 24.5 cm^3. In the gaseous state at ordinary pressures, therefore, the molecules are so far apart (except during their brief collisions) that their intrinsic volumes and their mutual attractions have little effect upon their behavior. We can accordingly set up as a "model"

[*] *Ann. Physik* **99,** 315 (1856).
[†] *Phil. Mag.* **14,** 108 (1857).

TABLE 2.1 Molar Volumes of Gases at 0° C and 1 atm
           (In cubic centimeters)

Argon	22,401	Neon	22,414
Helium	22,396	Nitrogen	22,403
Hydrogen	22,432	Oxygen	22,392

or "reference state" an "ideal" or "perfect" gas whose molecules posses mass and velocity but only negligible size and attractive forces. The properties of actual gases approach those of the ideal gas more and more closely the lower the pressure and the higher the temperature. A mole of ideal gas obeys the relation $PV/RT = 1$. The behavior of a particular gas can be expressed in terms of departures from that of an ideal gas. One such way is to evaluate one or more of the terms of the equation

$$Pv/RT = 1 + B/v^2 + C/v^3 + \ldots$$

(We will henceforth designate volume per mole by v_1, *unrestricted* volume by V.) The use of reference states is a valuable method for expressing the properties of an actual system. Other examples of reference states include the "ideal solution," the "regular solution" (see Chapter 4), and the "standard state" of a substance.

This chapter deals with the behavior of the ideal gas; actual gases are discussed in Chapter 3. However, the relations we now develop can serve to predict the behavior of an actual gas with a degree of accuracy that is adequate for many purposes. They serve also as norms for expressing more precisely the properties of real gases, where molecular sizes and attractive forces play important roles.

According to postulates of the kinetic molecular theory, gases exert pressure by virtue of the random chaotic motion of their molecules. The pressure exerted by a gas at the confining walls of its container is assumed to arise from impacts made there by molecules of the gas. If the container is isolated from its surroundings, the gas pressure reaches a particular value, which depends on the volume, the temperature, and the amount of gas. This is the *equilibrium pressure*. It is independent of time in an isolated system, and in order to account for this experimental observation, one needs to postulate that collisions of the gas molecules with one another and with the walls are perfectly elastic; that is, the molecular kinetic energy is conserved during collision. The kinetic energy of a single molecule is in general changed by collision, but any increase or decrease in its energy is exactly balanced by a corresponding decrease or increase in the energy of the other molecule or molecules taking part in the collision. Still another postulate is necessary to account for the specific relationships of Boyle and Charles among the pressure, volume, and temperature of a given mass of an ideal gas. It suffices to assume that the average kinetic energy per molecule (designated $\bar{\epsilon}_k$) of the molecules of a gas at equilibrium is a function only of the absolute temperature and in fact is directly proportional to it.

$$\bar{\epsilon}_k = \alpha T \tag{2.1}$$

where α is a proportionality constant. The need for this postulate is made readily apparent by the following considerations. If the volume of a sample of gas is halved while the temperature is held constant, then by eq. 2.1 the average kinetic energy and hence the average molecular speed are unchanged. The average force acting on the wall from a single molecular impact is unchanged, but because of the reduced volume, the frequency of impacts and hence the pressure are doubled. This is Boyle's law. If the absolute temperature of a gas maintained at constant volume is doubled, then by eq. 2.1 the average kinetic energy is doubled. That this increase in energy is exactly enough to double the pressure (Charles' law) is easily demonstrated by calculation of the changes in frequency and in average force of molecular impacts at the wall. These calculations are suggested as an interesting exercise for the student.

Derivation of the Basic Equation

Thus far we have considered only qualitative aspects of the kinetic theory. The average molecular kinetic energy of a gas depends only on the absolute temperature, and the equilibrium pressure of a gas depends on mechanical properties (mass, velocity, number density) of the molecules themselves. It is instructive to consider how one can determine the value of α in eq. 2.1 and the exact analytical relationship between pressure and mechanical variables. To find the answers it is necessary first to consider in more detail the mechanism whereby gaseous pressure is generated.

We may define the pressure on a small area of the wall of a gas-filled container as the magnitude of the force acting perpendicular to the wall in that region, divided by the area. Pressure then is equal to and has the same dimensions as force/area or (by Newton's second law of motion) as mass × acceleration/area. Acceleration is the time rate of change of the velocity, which is designated $\Delta u/\Delta t$ (see page 4) where Δu is the change in velocity u during the very small time interval Δt. The momentum of a moving object is by definition equal to its mass times its velocity; we shall designate it by the symbol $\varphi = mu$. The expression for the pressure can then be written

$$p = m(\Delta u_{\perp}/\Delta t)\,(1/A)$$

where $u_{\perp}$ is the component of velocity perpendicular to the area A. Since m is considered to be a constant, $m\Delta u = \Delta\varphi$, and

$$p = (1/A)\,(\Delta\varphi_{\perp}/\Delta t)$$

Thus gas pressure is equal to the time rate of change of momentum perpendicular to the wall divided by the area. Our task of calculating the equilibrium pressure of a gas is to evaluate the terms in the right-hand side of the above expression.

Consider a gas composed of N molecules, each of mass m, confined in a cubical box having edge length equal to L cm. Assume for the present that the walls of the box are rigid and plane, so that gas molecules are scattered from them as light rays from a plane mirror. Set up an x, y, z coordinate axis so that the origin coincides with one corner of the box, and three of the edges lie along the axis (Fig. 2.1).

Now consider one of the molecules. Assume it has an initial velocity u. Its components of motion along the three directions x, y, and z are given by u_x, u_y, and u_z, respectively. By elementary considerations the magnitude of the velocity u is equal to the length of a body-diagonal of a rectangular paral-

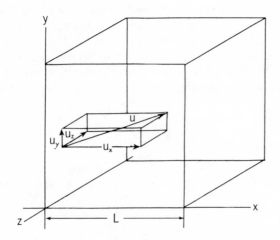

Fig. 2.1 Model for calculation of equilibrium gas pressure.

lelepiped having edges of lengths u_x, u_y, and u_z. This gives

$$u^2 = u_x^2 + u_y^2 + u_z^2 \tag{2.2}$$

When this molecule collides with a wall of the box, that component of its velocity which is directed at right angles to the wall is exactly reversed by the collision, while the other components of motion are unaltered. Let us consider collisions of this molecule with the left-hand wall of the box, that is, with the yz plane. If velocities from left to right along the x direction are taken to be positive, the molecule approaches the wall with perpendicular velocity $-u_x$ and momentum $-mu_x$. It rebounds from the wall with perpendicular velocity u_x and momentum mu_x. The change in perpendicular momentum per collision with the left-hand wall for this molecule is

$$\Delta \varphi_\perp = \varphi_{\perp \text{ (final)}} - \varphi_{\perp \text{ (final)}} = mu_x - (-mu_x) = 2mu_x$$

After collision the molecule must move a distance $2L$ in the x direction before making another impact on the left-hand wall. Since its x component of velocity is unchanged, this round trip takes $2L/u_x$ sec, and the collision frequency of this molecule with the left-hand wall is $u_x/2L$ sec^{-1}. The contribution to the pressure at the left-hand wall due to collisions there by this molecule is equal to the total change in momentum of the molecule suffered at the wall in one second divided by the area of the wall, L^2. Let us call this contribution to the pressure p_1. Then

$$p_1 = mu_x^2/L^3 \tag{2.3}$$

The total pressure, P, exerted on the left-hand wall is simply the sum of contributions of this type over all the molecules present in the box.

$$\begin{aligned} P &= p_1 + p_2 + \ldots + p_N \\ &= (m/L^3)(u_{x_1}^2 + u_{x_2}^2 + \ldots + u_{x_N}^2) \end{aligned} \tag{2.4}$$

Now multiply and divide the right-hand side of eq. 2.4 by N.

$$P = (Nm/L^3)[(u_{x_1}{}^2 + u_{x_2}{}^2 + \cdots + u_{x_N}{}^2)/N] \tag{2.5}$$

The term in brackets is clearly equal to the average value of the square of the x component of velocity, which may be written $\overline{u_x{}^2}$. Therefore

$$P = Nm\,\overline{u_x{}^2}/L^3 \tag{2.6}$$

A fundamental idea of the kinetic molecular theory is that of utter chaos of molecular motion for gases in equilibrium; thus for such a gas there is no preferred direction of motion. The average velocity of the molecules in one direction is the same as that in any other direction; and therefore

$$\overline{u_x{}^2} = \overline{u_y{}^2} = \overline{u_z{}^2} \tag{2.7}$$

Substitution of this expression into eq. 2.2 gives

$$\overline{u_x{}^2} = \tfrac{1}{3}\overline{u^2} \tag{2.8}$$

Equations 2.6 and 2.7 give

$$P = Nm\,\overline{u^2}/3L^3 \tag{2.9}$$

Now L^3 is just the volume, V, of the box so that we get finally

$$P = Nm\overline{u^2}/3V \tag{2.10}$$

In the above equations $\overline{u^2}$ is the average value of the square of the velocity, usually called the mean square velocity. It is important to note that the mean square velocity is not equal to the square of the average velocity (i.e., $\overline{u^2} \neq \bar{u}^2$), and consequently $\sqrt{\overline{u^2}}$, called the root mean square velocity, u_{rms}, is not equal to $\bar{u}$, the average velocity. Slightly more detailed considerations of the kinetic theory than are presented here show that u_{rms} is about 8.5 per cent greater than $\bar{u}$ for a gas in equilibrium.

Equation 2.10 above is the desired expression relating

equilibrium pressure to the mechanical properties of the gas. The value of the parameter α in eq. 2.1 is now easily found by comparing eq. 2.10 with the ideal gas law

$$P = nRT/V \tag{2.11}$$

where n is the number of moles of gas present and is equal to N/N_0 (N_0 is Avogadro's number and is equal to 6.02×10^{23} molecules mole^{-1}). The ideal gas law can then be written

$$P = NRT/N_0 V \tag{2.12}$$

Derived Relations

The Boltzmann Constant.   Equating eqs. 2.10 and 2.12 gives

$$mu^2/3 = RT/N_0 \tag{2.13}$$

The kinetic energy of a molecule at any instant is given by

$$\epsilon_k = \tfrac{1}{2}mu^2 \tag{2.14}$$

The average kinetic energy per molecule is simply

$$\overline{\epsilon_k} = \tfrac{1}{2}m(u_1{}^2 + u_2{}^2 + \cdots + u_N{}^2)/N = \tfrac{1}{2}m\overline{u^2} \tag{2.15}$$

Substitution of eq. 2.15 into eq. 2.13 gives

$$\overline{\epsilon_k} = \tfrac{3}{2}(R/N_0)T \tag{2.16}$$

Thus, by comparison with eq. 2.1, we see that α is equal to $\tfrac{3}{2}(R/N_0)$. The factor R/N_0, the ratio of two constants, occurs very frequently in physical science; it is usually designated by the symbol **k** and called the *Boltzmann constant*. It is clear that **k** is the gas law constant referred to one molecule instead of one mole. Introducing this notation we find

$$\alpha = \tfrac{3}{2}\mathbf{k} \tag{2.17}$$

and

$$\overline{\epsilon_k} = \tfrac{3}{2}\mathbf{k}T \tag{2.18}$$

The total average translational kinetic energy for one mole of a gas at the temperature T is

$$\bar{E}_k = \mathcal{N}_0\bar{\epsilon}_k = \tfrac{3}{2}(\mathcal{N}_0\mathbf{k})T = \tfrac{3}{2}RT \qquad (2.19)$$

Since R is about 2 cal mole^{-1} deg^{-1}, the molar translational kinetic energy of a gas at room temperature (about $300°$ K) is approximately 900 cal mole^{-1}.

Dalton's Law. Since the molecules of a gas act independently, the total kinetic energy of $\mathcal{N}$ molecules is the sum of all the individual kinetic energies, and hence the total pressure is additive. This is true even if molecules are not all of the same species. This is *Dalton's law: the total pressure of a mixture of gases is the sum of the partial pressures* of the gases present. The partial pressures are the pressures each species would exert if it alone were present. For example, if two vessels containing oxygen and nitrogen at the same pressure and temperature are connected so that the gases can mix, no change in pressure will occur.

Avogadro's Rule. Equation 2.10 provided the theoretical basis that transforms Avogadro's "hypothesis," as it was when announced in 1811, into Avogadro's "rule," or "law," which states that equal volumes of two different gases at the same pressure and temperature contain the same number of molecules. If $T_1 = T_2$, $m_1\overline{u_1^2} = m_2\overline{u_2^2}$, $P_1 = P_2$, $V_1 = V_2$, then $\mathcal{N}_1 = \mathcal{N}_2$. As put forward by Avogadro, in 1811, it was essentially a hypothesis. Its great significance was not appreciated until Cannizzaro explained it in 1860. It provided the basis for determining the proper formulas of elements and compounds and the values to use for atomic weights.

The first book on chemistry encountered by this author was "A Class Book of Chemistry" by Edward L. Youmans, published by D. Appleton and Co., New York, in "M.DCCCLVII." Its Table of Elementary Substances includes the following "atomic weights": C, 6; Fe, 28; O, 8;

S, 16. Water is HO; "dicarburet of hydrogen" is H_2C; sulfuric acid is SO_2HO. Cannizzaro was the first to bring order out of this confusion, although the way to this clarification had been open for forty-seven years!

Gay-Lussac's Law. A corollary of Avogadro's law is Gay-Lussac's law, although it antedated Avogadro's law by three years. It states that gases react in simple multiple proportions by volume. For example,

$$2SO_2 + O_2 = 2SO_3$$

Relative vols.:   2   1   2

The author has a strong sentimental regard for Gay-Lussac's law because he was able to use it, in 1899, while in high school, to find out whether the formula for nitric oxide should be written NO or N_2O_2, as it was in the textbook by Professor Josiah Cooke, of Harvard, entitled "Chemical Philosophy" (a relic of the time when all natural science was "natural philosophy"). This was a crucial experiment because Cooke maintained that an element must be either an "artiad" or "perissad"; that is, its valences must all be either even or odd.

The then juvenile author collected nitric oxide and oxygen over water in graduated tubes. He poured the former into an excess of the latter, so as to be sure to produce N_2O_4, not N_2O_3. This dissolved in the water. The result was that two volumes of nitric oxide reacted with one volume of oxygen:

$$2NO + O_2 = N_2O_4 \quad \text{(dissolved)}$$

relative volumes 2 to 1; not

$$N_2O_2 + O_2 = N_2O_4$$

relative volumes 1 to 1.

The experimenter was most fortunate to discover at this early stage of his scientific career that the final authority in science is a well-planned and reasoned experiment, not a book or a professor. This is a basic characteristic of physical science.

Absolute Molecular Velocities. Equation 2.10 can be used to obtain still another interesting result, the absolute root mean square velocities of molecules. We guard against error best by expressing all quantities in the c.g.s. system, where 1 atmosphere is 1.0133×10^6 dynes cm^{-2}. We use $\mathcal{N}_0 = 6.02 \times 10^{23}$ molecules, and $v = 22,400$ cm^3 mole^{-1}. Let us begin with hydrogen, where $\mathcal{N}_0 m = 2.016$ g. Transforming eq. 2.10

$$u_{rms} = [(3 \times 1.033 \times 10^{-6} \times 2.24 \times 10^4)/2.016]^{1/2}$$

$$= 1.84 \times 10^5 \text{ cm sec}^{-1}$$

This is 1.84 km sec^{-1}, or 1.14 miles sec^{-1}.

The molal weight of oxygen is 32.0 g, which is 16 times that of hydrogen; hence, the mean molecular velocity of oxygen molecules at 0° C is $\frac{1}{4} \times 1.84$, or 0.46 km sec^{-1}.

It should be remembered that these are *mean square* velocities, and that actual velocities are distributed over a considerable range. The calculation of this distribution is complex and beyond the scope of this book. Fig. 2.2 gives the calculated distribution of velocities for nitrogen at 0 and 1000° C.

The change in this distribution with temperature often plays an important role in determining the speed of a chemical reaction. It is usually not enough for two molecules to collide in order to react; the energy of collision must be sufficiently high to "activate" the reacting molecules; therefore the speed of the reaction depends upon the fraction of the molecules which possess energy in excess of the activation. This fraction rises at a much faster rate than the Kelvin temperature.

Experiments have been performed to verify a formula derived by Maxwell for the distribution of velocities about their root means square value. The various pieces of apparatus used for the purpose have all been designed so as to spread

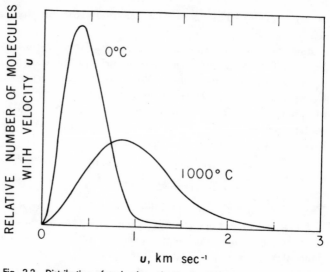

Fig. 2.2 Distribution of molecular velocities in nitrogen at 0 and 1000° C.

individual velocities by devices essentially the same in principle as one that might be used to get the variations in the velocities of individual particles from a shotgun. If the gun is held still and the target is on the surface of a cylinder rotating with a peripheral speed of the same order of magnitude as the mean speed of the shot, then the dots on the target will be spread in a pattern of density like that in Fig. 2.2.

The velocity that a moving body must exceed in order to escape from the gravitational field of the earth is approximately 7 miles sec^{-1}, or 11 km sec^{-1}. Reference to Fig. 2.2 shows that virtually no molecules of nitrogen, or even of hydrogen, have velocities sufficient to enable them to escape from our atmosphere. The escape velocity from the moon, however, is 1.5 miles sec^{-1}, or 2.4 km sec^{-1}. The surface of the moon gets rather hot on its bright side, and we can easily see why the moon has no atmosphere.

Heat Capacities. Degrees of Freedom:
Translational, Rotational, Vibrational

Let us now pursue further the relation between gas kinetic
energy and RT expressed in eq. 2.19.

In the case of molecules consisting of only one atom, a rise
in temperature can serve only to increase their translational
kinetic energy, and hence the heat capacity per mole at constant volume

$$c_v = \Delta E_k / \Delta T = \tfrac{3}{2}R \qquad (2.20)$$

For the monatomic gases of Group 0 and mercury, $c_v \cong 3.0$
cal deg^{-1} mole^{-1}.

If a gas is allowed to expand upon heating in such a way as
to keep the pressure constant, the gas must absorb heat in
addition to c_v equivalent to the work $P(V_2 - V_1)$. For 1 mole
of gas heated 1 deg, this is $R(T + 1) - RT = R$; therefore
the molal heat capacity at constant pressure exceeds c_v by R
cal deg^{-1} mole^{-1}.

$$c_p - c_v = R \qquad (2.21)$$

For a monatomic gas, then, the ratio

$$c_p/c_v = \tfrac{5}{3} = \gamma \qquad (2.22)$$

The symbol γ (Greek gamma) is commonly used for this
ratio.

A diatomic molecule can take up not only energy of transla-
tion, e_k, but also energy of rotation, e_{rot}, and of vibration, e_{vib}.
All molecules are free to move in the three "dimensions" x,
y, and z and are said to have three "degrees of freedom," in
each of which they have, accordingly, the energy $\tfrac{1}{2}R$.

A monatomic molecule does not have a "rough" surface
and cannot be set spinning by a glancing blow. Similarly,
neither a diatomic molecule nor a longer, rigid, linear mole-

cule such as CO_2 can aquire any energy by spinning around its long axis.

The number of rotational degrees of freedom of a molecule is equal to the *minimum* number of rotational axes through the center of mass of the molecule in terms of which all possible rotational patterns of the molecule may be described. There are many ways that such axes can be chosen; in determining the rotational freedom of a molecule it is necessary only to select a minimum set. One convenient way to do this is to set up x, y, z axes with the origin at the molecular center of mass. For linear molecules imagine the z axis to lie along the line joining the atomic nuclei. The molecule then has appreciable moments of inertia about only the x and y axes, and consequently it can have only two modes of rotational freedom. If each of these absorbs energy at the same rate as a translational degree of freedom, the rotational energy for a gas composed of linear molecules is RT per mole.

Nonlinear polyatomic molecules have appreciable moments of inertia about three independent axes and hence have three degrees of rotational freedom and rotational energy equal to $\frac{3}{2}RT$ mole^{-1} when fully excited.

Polyatomic molecules can also vibrate. A diatomic molecule can vibrate only along its bond axis. Carbon dioxide (a linear triatomic molecule) has two longitudinal modes of vibration and two transverse modes in planes at right angles to each other, as illustrated in Fig. 2.3. Each mode has two degrees of freedom, one for potential energy and one for kinetic energy. It is evident that as molecular complexity increases c_v, and of course c_p, rise rapidly, and γ falls from its maximum of 1.67 toward 1.0.

The temperatures at which these various degrees of freedom are excited vary in accord with the predictions of quantum theory. Hydrogen, whose heat capacity can be measured at lower temperatures than that of any other diatomic gas, has

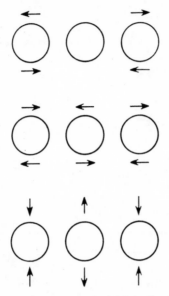

Fig. 2.3 Modes of molecular vibration for CO_2.

values of $c_v = 3.0$ cal mole^{-1} deg^{-1}, like He, below $\sim 50°$K, as seen in Fig. 2.4, after which it rapidly rises to the value $c_v = 5.0$ cal mole^{-1} deg^{-1} for $e_k + e_{rot}$. For the diatomic molecules H_2, N_2, NO, O_2, in the region of ordinary temperatures, $c_v = 5.0$ cal mole^{-1} deg^{-1}, $c_p = 7.0$ cal mole^{-1} deg^{-1}, $\gamma = 1.40$. We see, however, that at very high temperatures, c_v rises above 5.0, more rapidly for H_2 than for N_2. Quantum theory teaches that energy is absorbed in quanta that are related to frequency of rotation, vibration, etc., and to the separation of "levels" of energy. Now the triple bond of a nitrogen molecule is much stronger than the single bond of a hydrogen molecule; their energies of dissociation are 226 and 103.7 kcal mole^{-1}, respectively. The greater stiffness of the N_2 bond requires that higher temperatures be reached before appreciable en-

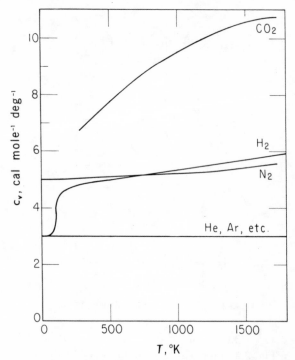

Fig. 2.4   Variation with temperature of molar heat capacity at constant volume.

ergy is absorbed in the vibrational modes. The frequencies and energies of vibration of both nitrogen and hydrogen are much higher than those of rotation; therefore c_v remains close to 5.0 cal mole^{-1} deg^{-1} over a considerable range of temperature.

Carbon dioxide, as can be seen in Fig. 2.4, has considerable internal energy at ordinary temperature, and c_v rapidly rises from 6.8 cal mole^{-1} deg^{-1} at 300°K to 10.5 cal mole^{-1} deg^{-1} at 1500°K.

The increase in values of c_v accompanying increasing molecular complexity means decrease in the figures for γ, as illustrated in Table 2.2. The determination of γ for argon, the first

TABLE 2.2   Decrease in Values of $\gamma = c_p/c_v$ (at 20°C) with Increasing Molecular Complexity

He, Ar, Hg	1.67	CO_2	1.30
N_2, O_2, NO, CO	1.40	SO_2	1.29
NH_3	1.32	C_2H_6	1.20

of the rare gases to be discovered, proved its monatomic nature, a fact that could not be established by volume relations in any chemical reaction.

Work of Expansion

In Isothermal Evolution or Absorption of Gas. Let us now consider the energy changes connected with volume and pressure changes of a gas. A gas may do work or have work done upon it in several ways. The simplest is the work done against atmospheric pressure by the vapor of a boiling liquid, or by the gas evolved at constant pressure by a chemical reaction. Suppose, for example, that oxygen is being evolved by heating mercuric oxide in a cylinder provided with a weighted piston, as depicted in principle in Fig. 2.5. The temperature is to be kept constant as oxygen is evolved, pushing the piston upward against the pressure of the atmosphere. Every mole of oxygen thus produced does work against the atmospheric pressure equal to $Pv = RT$.

If ammonia is decomposed by continued sparking, the reaction is $2NH_3 = N_2 + 3H_2$. The volume after the reaction is complete, if measured at the same temperature and pressure as the ammonia, would have doubled; the volume of two moles of gas would have increased to four moles of gas; and the work done would be $2RT$.

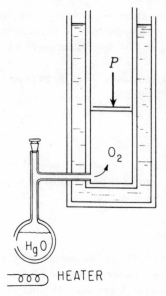

Fig. 2.5 The work done by a gas
evolving against atmospheric pressure at a constant temperature.

In Isothermal Expansion or Compression per Mole of Gas.   Let
us now consider the expansion or compression of a fixed
quantity of gas in a cylinder provided with a piston. If the
piston is at rest, gas molecules striking it rebound, on the
average, with the same velocity, since the molecules in the
piston are at the same temperature and hence have the same
mean kinetic energy as those of the gas. The angle at which
an individual molecule rebounds is not necessarily the same as
its angle of incidence, because the rebound is from the molecules of the wall, not from a smooth surface. The angles of
rebound equal the angles of incidence, not individually, but
on the average.

Suppose, next, that the piston is pushed in, compressing the gas. As the piston advances, it has the effect upon the impinging molecules that a bat has when swung to hit a pitched ball; the molecules rebound with increased kinetic energy. An alert reader may ask, how can a slowly advancing piston have much effect upon the velocity of rebound of a molecule moving at, perhaps, half a mile a second? The answer is that it has very little accelerative effect upon a single rebound; but we are not considering a single impact. The reader may be more impressed if he calculates the number of impacts per square centimeter per second upon the walls by the molecules of, say, nitrogen at 27°C and 1 atm. And if the piston advances more slowly, the individual rebounds gain less energy, but there are more of them. Of course, the energy absorbed from the advancing piston is soon given up to the walls of the container; hence the piston must advance at high speed in order to produce the maximum rise in temperature. We return to this a little later.

Let us first have our piston advance or retreat slowly enough for heat to leak out or in from a surrounding water jacket which maintains constant temperature. Here, again, the work of expansion or compression is simply the product of force acting through a distance. P and V are now both changing, but in agreement with Boyle's law. We may calculate the work by using the procedure many readers have doubtless learned from the calculus, which is to "integrate" the work done by the pressure operating through infinitesimal increments of volume, PdV, between the limits V and V'. The work of compressing gas from V_1 to V_2 is then

$$\int_{V_1}^{V_2} -PdV = -RT \int_{V_1}^{V_2} dV/V = RT \ \ln V_1/V_2 \qquad (2.23)$$

Since $P \propto 1/V$, this can be written $RT \ln P_2/P_1$. Here ln denotes the logarithm to the base e. To convert to common logarithms we multiply by the factor 2.3026.

If, for example, a mole of gas is compressed from 100 liters to 10 liters, at $T = 300°K$, the work involved is

$$2.3026 \times 300 \times 0.082 \log 10 = 56.6 \text{ liter atm}$$

If we wish the equivalent in calories, we use $R = 1.986$ cal mole^{-1} deg^{-1}.

Adiabatic Expansion and Compression. The third case to consider is expansion or compression so rapid that there is no time to restore the original mean kinetic energy of the molecules by any exchange of heat with the surroundings. Such a process is called *adiabatic*.

If a piston is suddenly pushed in so as to diminish the volume of the contained gas to one half, the pressure, which would be doubled in an isothermal compression, is now more than doubled by the accompanying rise in temperature. The magnitude of this rise is maximum with a monatomic gas; it is less with a diatomic gas, since some of the energy of compression can be absorbed by rotation and vibration of diatomic molecules. The more complex the molecule, the smaller the fraction of energy of compression that appears as translational kinetic energy, i.e., as increase in temperature. The heating is at a maximum for monatomic molecules, where $\gamma = 1.67$. But as the number of atoms per molecule increases, this ratio falls, becoming 1.40 for diatomic molecules, and still less for more complex species.

To reduce these relations to a strictly quantitative basis requires some acquaintance with thermodynamics, the discipline relating energy, heat, and work, but the foregoing discussion should, in the meantime, make the following relations for adiabatic expansion and compression seem reasonable.

Instead of Boyle's law, we have

$$P/P_0 = (V_0/V)^{R/c_v} \qquad (2.24)$$

Instead of Charles' law, we have

$$T/T_0 = (P/P_0)^{R/c_p} \qquad (2.25)$$

A simple way to represent either of these relations is to plot the logarithm of one member against the logarithm of the other, using the value of γ or c_p appropriate to the gas in question. For a diatomic gas, eq. 2.25 becomes

$$\log T/T_0 = \tfrac{2}{7} \log P/P_0 \qquad (2.26)$$

Figure 2.6 illustrates the rises in temperature it is possible to attain by adiabatic compression calculated by aid of eq.

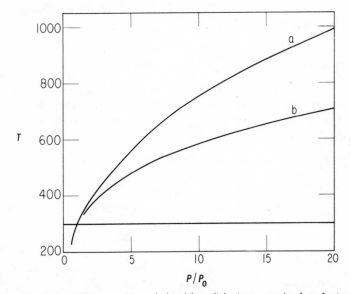

Fig. 2.6 Kelvin temperatures calculated for adiabatic compression from 1 atm at $T = 300°$ to pressures P/P_0 for (a) monatomic gases and (b) diatomic gases.

2.25 starting at $T = 300°K$. The upper curve applies to monatomic, the lower to diatomic, molecules. Values of P/P_0 less than unity represent adiabatic cooling.

There were primitive men who discovered this interesting phenomenon and applied it to obtain fire. A hollow wooden cylinder was fitted with a piston, tinder was placed in the cylinder, and the piston was struck by a blow of enough force to raise the air to a temperature sufficient to ignite the tinder. If primitive men were smart enough to discover and apply adiabatic heating, a modern student should be smart enough at least to grasp the principle of it.

Present-day scientists are studying gas reactions at the high temperatures that can be produced by "shock waves." They thus avoid the difficulties involved in devising vessels that can withstand high temperatures.

The gas mixture in a Diesel engine is ignited by adiabatic compression, not by a spark.

Velocity of Sound

A sound wave consists of alternating compressions and rarefactions so rapid as to be adiabatic, and hence the velocity of sound depends upon γ, the ratio c_p/c_v, and is highest in a monatomic gas. The formula is

$$U = (\gamma RT/M)^{1/2} \tag{2.27}$$

For air, treated as a diatomic gas, at $T = 300°K$, this gives

$$U = [1.40 \times (8.3 \times 10^7 \times 300)/28.8]^{1/2}$$
$$= 3.48 \times 10^4 \text{ cm sec}^{-1}$$

or 1140 feet sec^{-1}, or 600 miles hour^{-1}.

The velocity of sound is simply related to root mean square molecular velocity. Eq. 2.10 can be written

$$\bar{u}^2 = 3RT/M \tag{2.28}$$

Combining this with eq. 2.27 gives

$$U/\bar{u} = (\gamma/3)^{1/2} \qquad (2.29)$$

For air, $c_p = 7$ cal mole^{-1} deg^{-1}, $c_v = 5$ cal mole^{-1} deg^{-1}, and $U = 0.20\,\bar{u}$.

The velocity of sound plays an important role in the behavior of high-speed airplanes, rockets, and missiles. The energy imparted to the air by the wing of an airplane moving at right angles to the direction of flight at speeds above the velocity of sound creates a "shock wave" of high energy. The "mach number" is the ratio of the speed of the moving body to the speed of sound.

Equation 2.29 can be used to calculate γ from determinations of the velocity of sound in the gas in question. This velocity can be measured in a horizontal closed tube containing the gas or vapor together with a light powder sprinkled along the tube. Sound from a tuning fork of known frequency impinging upon a flexible diaphragm at one end of the tube sets up standing waves that collect the powder at nodes, whose distance apart is one half of the wavelength, which, multiplied by the frequency, gives the velocity.

Variation of Atmospheric Pressure and Temperature with Altitude

The atmospheric pressure at sea level is the weight of all the air in a column 1 cm^2 in cross section extending upward to empty space. At any altitude, h, above sea level, h_0, the pressure is less by the weight of air between h and h_0. The rate at which the pressure diminishes with increasing height is determined by the weight of air per cubic centimeter, which is Mg/V, where M is the mass and v the volume of 1 mole of air, and g is the acceleration due to gravity. The mean molal mass of air is about 28.8 grams. The molal volume is RT/P.

Consequently,

$$- dP/dh = MgP/RT \tag{2.30}$$

(For the reader who is not acquainted with the symbols used in calculus, dP and dh indicate infinitesimal increments of pressure and height, respectively. The minus sign is used because pressure decreases as height increases.) Transforming gives

$$RTd \ln P = -Mgdh$$

Integrating from P_0 to P_h and h_0 to h at constant T gives

$$RT \ln P_h/P_0 = -Mg(h - h_0) \tag{2.31}$$

As an illustration let us calculate the ratio P/P_0 between the top and bottom of a hill 100 meters high. We must take care to use consistent units. In the c.g.s. system, $h - h_0 = 10^4$ cm; $R = 8.31 \times 10^7$ ergs deg^{-1} mole^{-1}; and $M = 28.8 \times 981 = 2.82 \times 10^4$ dynes. To convert natural to common logarithms, the factor is 2.303. Let us take $T = 293°$ K. These figures give log $P/P_0 = -0.00509$. Since P/P_0 is a ratio, we are free to use any units. Taking $P_0 = 760$ mm, log $P_0 = 2.88081$, log $P = 2.87572$, $P = 751.1$ mm, and $P_0 - P = 8.9$ mm, a very substantial difference. This illustrates how a barometer can serve to measure elevations with fair accuracy.

We assumed in the above calculation that there would be no appreciable difference in temperature between the bottom and top of a hill 100 meters high, and that eq. 2.31 is applicable. But if we are interested in the pressure at mountain tops, or at the altitudes of airplane flight, the temperature gradient must be taken into account.

As a mass of dry air ascends, the process approaches adiabatic, where the density accords with eqs. 2.25 and 2.26. If we use these relations in eq. 2.30 we obtain, by a moderately involved sequence,

$$P_h/P_0 = [1 - (R/c_p)(Mh/RT_0)]^{c_p/R} \tag{2.32}$$

The difference between P_h calculated by eqs. 2.31 and 2.32 is surprisingly small; at 5 km (16,400 ft, a very high mountain) the isothermal formula gives 0.56 atm, the adiabatic 0.53 atm.

The temperature and pressure gradients are both subject to considerable variation. Condensation of water vapor into clouds releases heat, and vice versa. Hot air masses ascend in "thermals," and these mix with colder air by turbulence at their boundaries. Cold and warm "fronts" invade the main masses. The barometric pressure varies with normal changes in weather by as much as 0.03 atm. Meteorologists have adapted a "Standard Atmosphere," reproduced in part in Table 2.3.

TABLE 2.3 The "Standard Atmosphere"

Altitude		Pressure (P/P_0)	t, °C
Kilometers	Feet		
0	0	1	15
1	3281	0.886	8.5
2	6562	0.784	2.0
3	9840	0.692	−4.5
4	13120	0.608	−11.0
5	16400	0.533	−17.5
6	19700	0.465	−24.0
8	26250	0.351	−37.0
10	32810	0.261	−50.0

Campers in mountainous regions have noticed the extra time required to cook food by boiling. At 3 km (9.840 ft), where the pressure fluctuates around 0.69 atm, water boils at 90°C. A 10° drop in temperature increases the time required for many slow reactions from two to three times.

Sedimentation Gradient

An historically very important adaptation of eq. 2.31 was made by Perrin, in 1910. He prepared by fractionation of suspensions of gamboge one sample whose particles were very uniform in size, each having mass m and density ρ. These particles, suspended in a liquid of density ρ_L, were acted upon by the opposing forces of Brownian motion and gravity. They distributed themselves with concentration diminishing upward. C_h and C_0, the concentrations of particles, are substituted for the P_h and P_0 of eq. 2.31. Considering the buoyancy of the liquid, the effective weight of a suspended spherical particle is

$$mg = \tfrac{4}{3}\pi r^3 g(\rho - \rho_L) \tag{2.33}$$

where r is the particle radius. The effective weight of a mole of such particles is

$$N_0 mg = \tfrac{4}{3}\pi r^3 N_0 g(\rho - \rho_L)$$

where N_0 is Avogadro's number. Introducing this notation, eq. 2.31 becomes

$$RT \ln C_h/C_0 = -\tfrac{4}{3}\pi r^3 N_0 g(\rho - \rho_L)(h - h_0) \tag{2.34}$$

By microscopic observation Perrin was able to count the numbers of particles suspended at the two heights h and h_0. The value of r was calculated from the density and mass of a known number of particles. From these results the value of N_0 in eq. 2.34 was determined. Perrin found $N_0 = 6.5 \times 10^{23}$, a number in good agreement with the currently accepted value. This experiment furnished one of the first direct evidences of molecular kinetic theory. The high value of m made the concentration gradient large enough to be observable with centimeter differences in height.

Exercises

Let us now practice with the foregoing concepts and relations so as to handle them with understanding and confidence. Let us consider a series of questions of gradually increasing complexity.

1. If a certain quantity of hydrogen occupies 100 cm^3 at 0.30 atm, at what pressure will it occupy 60 cm^3?

   Ans. First, is it obvious that a higher pressure will be required, since the gas is to be compressed. To compress to 60/100 of its first volume requires an *increase* in pressure to 0.30 × 100/60, or 0.50 atm.

2. A flask contains 2.00 g of gas at 57° C and 1 atm. At what temperature would it contain 3.30 g of the same gas at a pressure of 1 atm?

   Ans. If the amount of gas is to be increased from 2.00 to 3.30 g, that is, by a factor of 33/20, without changing the pressure, the mean kinetic energy, and hence the absolute temperature, must be *decreased* to 330 × 20/33, or 200° K (this is −73° C).

3. If an automobile tire is inflated to 20 psi gage pressure when cold, at 15° C, what will it become if the tire is heated to 30° C by running?

   Ans. A tire gage measures not the pressure of the air inside but its *excess* over the pressure of the external atmosphere, which we can take for this purpose as 14.7 psi (pounds per square inch). A gage pressure of 20 psi thus indicates a total pressure of 34.7 psi. The temperature is 15 + 273 = 288° K. If the tire temperature becomes 30° C, or 303° K, the kinetic energy of the molecules, and hence the pressure within the tire, is increased by a factor of 303/288, and (303/288) × 34.7 psi = 36.4 psi. The gage pressure will then be 36.4 − 14.7 = 21.7 psi.

4. What per cent of the air in the tire would then have to be let out in order to reduce to pressure to the original 20 psi?

   Ans. The excess pressure is 1.7 psi, and this is 1.7/21.7 of the air in the tire, or 7.85 per cent.

5. Given the relations below on the left between the variables for two gases, what can you conclude regarding the variables on the right?

Given	Infer (>, <, or ?)
(a) Equal P, V, T, $M_1 > M_2$	$\bar{u}_1 \ldots \bar{u}_2$
(b) Equal P, V, T, $M_1 > M_2$	$N_1 \ldots N_2$
(c) Equal P, V, $N_1 > N_2$	$T_1 \ldots T_2$
(d) Equal T, N, $P_1 > P_2$, $M_1 > M_2$	$V_1 \ldots V_2$
(e) Equal V, N, $\bar{u}$, $M_1 > M_2$	$P_1 \ldots P_2$

Ans. Case (a): If $T_1 = T_2$, then regardless of P and V, the kinetic energies are equal, and if $M_1 > M_2$, $\bar{u}_1 < \bar{u}_2$.

Case (b): Two gases at the same P, V, T contain the same number of molecules regardless of molecular weights.

Case (c): In order for the pressures to be the same in equal volumes, the vessel containing the larger number of molecules must be at the lower temperature.

Case (d): If two gases contain the same number of molecules at the same temperature, the one at the higher pressure occupies the smaller volume, regardless of molecular weights.

Case (e): Since the two velocities are the same and the molecules of the first gas have smaller molecular weight, this one has the smaller kinetic energy, and $T_1 < T_2$. The concentration of the molecules is the same in both; therefore the one at higher temperature exerts the greater pressure.

5. If a 2.0 liter flask of N_2 at 20° C and 70 cm pressure is connected with a 3.00 liter flask of O_2 at the same temperature and 100 cm pressure, what will the final pressure be after the gases have thoroughly mixed and at the same temperature as before?

Ans. Since the molecules all act independently of each other, the final pressure is the sum of the pressures each of the two gases would exert alone in the expanded space. The N_2 has expanded from 2.00 liters to 5.00 liters; hence its partial pressure is $70 \times 2\frac{1}{5} = 28$ cm. The O_2 has expanded from 3.00 liters to 5.00 liters; therefore its partial pressure will be $100 \times 3/5 = 60$ cm. The total pressure will be $28 + 60 = 88$ cm.

6. What is the weight of 10.0 liters of methane, CH_4, at 0.5 atm and 17° C?

Ans. Since the volume of 1 mole of CH_4 at 273° K and 1 atm is 22.4 liters, at 300° K and 0.5 atm it would become $22.4 \times (300/273) \times 2 = 49.2$ liters. It weighs 16.0 g per mole; therefore 10.0 liters under these conditions would weigh $16.0 \times (10.0/49.2) = 3.25$ g.

The same result could be obtained by allowing gas to escape upon raising the temperature and reducing the volume, as follows. Since 22.4 liters at 273° K and 1 atm weighs 16.0 g, 10 liters at 300° K and 1 atm would weigh $16.0 \times (10.0/22.4) \times (273/300) \times 0.5 = 3.25$ g.

7. How far, approximately, can a diver descend breathing compressed air before the partial pressure of the oxygen he breathes exceeds 1 atm?

Ans. 1 atm supports 76 cm of mercury. The density of mercury is approximately 13.6 g cm^{-3}; therefore 1 atm is equivalent to 13.6 × 76 cm or 1030 cm of water. There are 2.54 cm in an inch; hence the column of water is 406 inches or 33.8 feet. Since oxygen is about 1/5 of the air, its partial pressure would become 1 atm at 5 atm air pressure or 5 × 34 ft = 170 ft.

8. State the effect upon (a) the rate of impacts per cm^2 upon the containing walls and (b) the average momentum of each impact of each of the following changes: H_2S is changed to H_2 by heating with zinc in a closed vessel and then cooled to the original temperature.

Ans. Since 1 mole of H_2S gives 1 mole of H_2, the number of molecules is unchanged. Since they are at the same T and P as the H_2S, the mean translational kinetic energy is the same. This is the number of impacts per square centimeter per second times the momentum of each impact. The H_2 molecule has a mass of 2; for H_2S the mass is 34. The mean velocity of the H_2 molecules is $(34/2)^{1/2}$ = 4.12 times that of the H_2S molecules; therefore H_2 molecules make 4.12 times as many impacts per second as those of H_2S. The ratio of the momentum of a molecule of H_2 to one of H_2S is 0.24, since $\bar{u}_2/\bar{u}_1$ = 4.12 and m_2/m_1 = 2/34. The average momentum is much less for H_2 than for H_2S.

9. Answer the same questions qualitatively for the air being compressed in a bicycle hand pump.

Ans. This is an adiabatic process, in which the air in the pump rises in temperature; hence the mean molecular kinetic energy is increased by increasing velocity, but not mass, and therefore the force of each impact is increased. The number of impacts per second per square centimeter is increased because of both increased molecular velocity and increased concentration of the molecules.

10. An airplane at normal cruising altitude is cooled by the air through which it passes; a rocket is heated. At what speed, in approximate miles per hour, is cooling replaced by heating?

Figure this out for yourself. Choose a plausible figure for temperature. Consider eq. 2.16.

11. If a bubble of air is formed under water at a depth of 10 m, by what factor does its volume increase just below the surface?

12. How much will air be cooled by sudden adiabatic expansion at 20° C from 5 to 2 atm?

13. Different gases have different efficiencies in conducting heat away from hot bodies. Explain.

14. Explain why cold but "damp" air feels more chilly than dry air at the same temperature.

15. Divers can operate at greater depths if they breathe a mixture of helium and oxygen instead of compressed air, but to use the former mixture it is necessary to provide electric heating of the diving suit. Why?

16. The MacLeod gage (see Fig. 2.7) is an apparatus for measuring low gas pressures. If the volume of B is 250 cm³, the diameter of the tube E is 1.0 mm, and $h'' - h = 50.0$ mm, what was the pressure of the gas in A?

Ans. This is a simple Boyle's law problem. The gas at first in B at the unknown pressure, P, is later in the capillary stem, D, at a pressure of $(h'' - h)$ mm; its volume is easily calculated from its diameter and $h' - h$.

17. What volume of air is necessary to burn 500 cm³ of H_2S gas, measured at the same temperature and pressure? The products are SO_2 and H_2O.

Ans. The equation must be

$$2H_2S + 3O_2 = 2H_2O + 2SO_2$$

Therefore $500 \times 3/2 = 750$ cm³ is the volume of O_2 that would be required. Since approximately 1/5 of the molecules of air are oxygen, $750 \times 5 = 3750$ cm³ of air would be required.

18. What volume would be occupied by 11.0 g of N_2O at 27° C and 700 mm pressure?

Ans. 1 mole of N_2O is 44.0 g; therefore 11.0 g is 0.25 mole, which would occupy $22.4/4 = 5.6$ liters at 273°K and 760 mm, $(300/273) \times 5.6$ liters at 300°K and 760 mm, and $(760/700) \times (300/273) \times 5.6$ liters at 300°K and 700 mm.

19. A closed flask contains ammonia at 1 atm and 25° C. A spark is passed through until all the ammonia is decomposed into nitro-

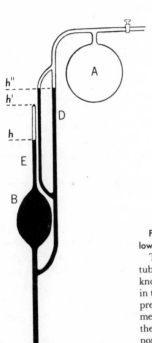

Fig. 2.7 MacLeod gage for measuring low gas pressures.

The volumes of the bulb B and of the tube E, per cm from the top down, are known. Mercury can be raised or lowered in the apparatus by applying or releasing pressure in the reservoir C. In order to measure the pressure of gas in bulb B, the mercury is lowered so as to allow a portion of the gas in A to stream into B. If pressure is very low, gas does not reach uniform pressure rapidly, so a little time should be allowed before forcing mercury up past the junction below B and into tube E. The gas that was in E is now all collected in D, in the volume between h and h', at a pressure given by $(h'' - h)$. From these figures the pressure of the gas initially in $(A + B)$ can easily be calculated.

gen and hydrogen. What will the pressure be after the contents are brought to 25° C?

Ans. The equation is

$$2NH_3 = N_2 + 3H_2$$

Therefore 2 moles of gas have increased to 4 moles to give a pressure of 4 atmospheres.

20. What are the specific gravities of the following gases referred to air at the same pressure and temperature: CO, Cl_2, NH_3, SO_2, H_2O?

Ans. Since approximately 1/5 of the molecules in air are O_2, a mole of air weighs $32 \times 1/5 + 28 \times 4/5 = 28.8$ g. Weights of equal volumes of other gases are heavier or lighter than air in the ratio their molal weights to 28.8.

20. What are the relative efficiencies of the following gases as filling for balloons: H_2, He, CH_4?

Ans. The lifting power of a balloon is the weight of the air it displaces less the weight of the gas it contains. For ballooms of equal volume, for example, 22.4 liters, at 0° C and 1 atm, these gases would lift the following loads, including the balloon itself: H_2, $28.8 - 2 = 26.8$ g; He, $28.8 - 4.0 = 24.8$ g; CH_4, $28.8 - 16.0 = 12.8$ g. Their efficiencies compared to H_2 are thus: He, 0.92; CH_4, 0.48.

21. How efficient is hot air for lifting a balloon? Make any reasonable assumptions.

22. A certain gas is known to contain 1 g of hydrogen to 12 g of carbon only, indicating that its formula must be CH or a multiple thereof. It is found that 295 cm^3 of it weighs 0.317 g at 22° C and 1 atm; what is its formula?

Ans. Its molal weight is the number of grams in 22,400 cm^3 at 273° K and 1 atm. Since 0.317 g at $22 + 273 = 295$° K and 1 atm has a volume of 295 cm^3, at 273°K its volume would be $295 \times 273/295 = 273$ cm^3. Since 273 cm^3 at standard conditions weighs 0.317 g, 22,400 cm^3 would weigh $0.317 \times 22,400/273$, or 26 g. This corresponds to C_2H_2.

REAL GASES

The van der Waals Equation of State

In Chapter 2 we dealt with properties of gases in regions of pressure and temperature where the intrinsic volume of all the molecules is so small in comparison with the volume occupied by the gas, and the molecules are so far apart between collisions, that molecular sizes and attractive forces can both be neglected when calculations of only moderate precision suffice. In this chapter, we look at these matters more critically, and at pressures and temperatures where deviations from the simple relations of the ideal gas must be taken into account. The magnitude of the deviations from the ideal gas laws at high pressures in the case of even very simple molecules is illustrated in Fig. 3.1.

The classic step taken to describe the behavior of real gases was that by van der Waals in 1881. Since the molecules of the gas have finite intrinsic volume, the space in which they are free to move is less than the volume of the container by an amount per mole designated by van der Waals by b. The molal volume of the gas thus becomes $(v - b)$. The molecules also attract each other, and this makes the pressure less than it would be for an ideal gas. Since binary collisions predominate until volumes become exceedingly small, the effect is proportional to $1/v^2$, and we write $(P + a/v^2)$, in-

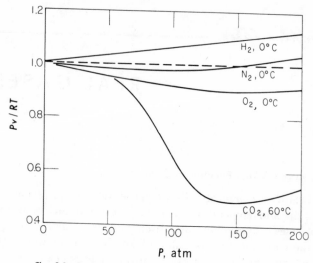

Fig. 3.1 Deviations from Boyle's law as pressure is increased.

stead of P. The van der Waals equation for 1 mole of gas is thus:

$$(P + a/v^2) \ (v - b) = RT \tag{3.1}$$

For n moles of gas it would be

$$(P + n^2a/v^2) \ (v - nb) = nRT \tag{3.2}$$

The relation of b to the volume of the molecules is as follows. Designating the diameter of a spherical molecule A in Fig. 3.2 by the Greek letter sigma, σ, the center of a second molecule of the same kind, B, cannot approach more closely than the distance σ to the center of the first molecule, as illustrated in Fig. 3.2. The center of B is therefore excluded from a spherical space around the center of A whose diameter is 2σ, and whose volume is four times the volume of A.

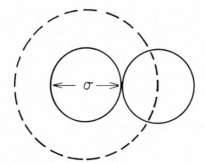

Fig. 3.2   Illustration of the "excluded volume" around a molecule from the fact that
the centers of two adjacent molecules cannot approach more closely than the molecular diameter σ.

It is instructive to compare the van der Waals equation of
state with a purely thermodynamic equation of state,

$$P + (\partial E/\partial V)_T = T(\partial P/\partial T)_V \qquad (3.3)$$

The term $(\partial E/\partial V)_T$ means simply the rate at which energy is
absorbed by a system when it is expanded in a thermostat so
as to maintain constant temperature.   It is a measure of cohesion, or "internal pressure."   Similarly, the term $(\partial P/\partial T)_V$
is the rate at which pressure increases with temperature when
volume is held constant.   It is R/v for a perfect gas, the constant of Charles' law.   When the system is a liquid or a gas,
this energy is absorbed in increasing the mean distance between molecules.   The correspondence between the terms of
eq. 3.3 and those of the van der Waals equation is easily seen
by writing the latter in the form

$$P + a/v^2 = TR/(v - b) \qquad (3.4)$$

The right-hand members of both equations represent what
may be called *thermal pressure*, or repulsion, the tendency of

the liquid or gas to expand. The left-hand terms represent the forces that oppose the tendency to fly apart; they are the *external pressure*, *P*, plus the *attractive pressure*, or "*internal pressure*," $(\partial E/\partial V)_T$ or a/v^2. The molecules of a mole of gas in 24,100 cm³ are on the average so far apart that cohesion is very small. In a liquid, on the other hand, *v* is so very much smaller that cohesion is very large. A mole of liquid CCl_4 at 25°C has a volume of 97 cm³ and $(\partial E/\partial V)_T = 3350$ atm.

One of the most striking features of the van der Waals equation is that it gives a rational connection between the liquid and gas states. In fact, the title of van der Waals' original publication (1881) was (translated) "The Continuity of the Gas and Liquid States." That it succeeds in this can be seen in Fig. 3.3, which shows *P* vs. *v* at four temperatures calculated for the parameters $a = 3.609 \times 10^6$ cm⁶ atm mole⁻² and $b = 42.75$ cm³ mole⁻¹. They were chosen so as to approximate the behavior of CO_2.

The equation can be rearranged as follows:

$$v^3 - (b + RT/P)v^2 + (a/P)v - ab/P = 0 \qquad (3.5)$$

This is a cubic equation in *v* and within certain ranges has three real values of *v*, illustrated by the points *B*, *E*, and *G* in Fig. 3.3. For the 31° isotherm, the three roots are real and equal; for the 40° isotherm, one root is real, two are imaginary.

Now we know that when vapors are compressed isothermally they reach a saturation point, after which, with further reduction in the volume, the vapor condenses to liquid at constant pressure along a path illustrated by *GEB*. At *B*, all the vapor has disappeared, and, the liquid being relatively incompressible, the further path, *BA*, is very steep. It is possible, upon taking great care to prevent the presence of nuclei for condensation, to continue a short distance on the van der Waals path to the left of *G* and, likewise, to stretch a com-

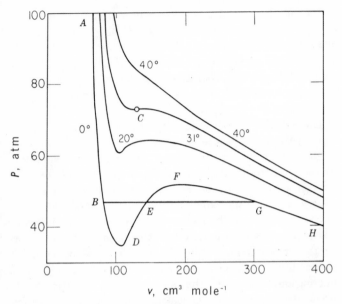

Fig. 3.3 The van der Waals paths between liquid and gas at various temperatures.

pletely enclosed liquid from B toward D. The path DEF is quite unrealizable, since it represents pressure *increasing* with volume. The pressure along the line BEG is, of course, fixed by the vapor pressure of liquid CO_2 at $0°C$.

The Critical Point

At the higher temperature, $20°C$, the region of three real roots is shorter, and at $31°C$ they have coalesced at C to the same value. At higher temperatures, only one root is real, corresponding to a single phase. This point is called the *critical point*. At still higher temperatures, the distinction between liquid and vapor has disappeared, and it would be possible to go from liquid over point C to GH continuously with only one phase present throughout.

The values of the van der Waals parameters, a and b, are simply related to the coordinates of the critical point, called critical pressure, P_c; critical volume, v_c; and critical temperature, T_c.

These can be experimentally determined. A liquid with its vapor, sealed in a glass tube strong enough to hold the critical pressure, is enclosed in an air bath at controlled temperature. As the temperature is slowly raised, the density of the vapor rises and the density of the liquid decreases. As the two phases approach the same density, the surface tension at the interface decreases; the surface flattens; refractive indices approach one another; and the interface becomes harder to see. At the critical temperature, the interface disappears. For several hundredths of a degree thereafter, there are minute fluctuations in density that give a milky appearance; the liquid is only quasihomogeneous. Only slightly higher temperatures suffice to make the fluid (no longer definitely either liquid or gas) quite clear and homogeneous.

The Law of Rectilinear Diameter

The relation between the densities of liquid and vapor as the critical temperature is approached is illustrated in Fig. 3.4 for ethylene. The two branches of the curve are bisected by a straight line. Cailletet and Mathias, in 1886, plotted the densities of many liquid–vapor systems in this way and found that the bisecting line is always straight; this relation is known as the *Law of Rectilinear Diameter*. The intersection of the diameter with the curve serves to fix the value of the critical volume. This is the sole reliable method for determining it.

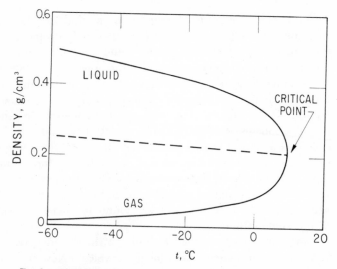

Fig. 3.4 Variation with temperature of the density of liquid and gaseous ethylene at equilibrium, and the "rectilinear diameter."

Determination of van der Waals Parameters from Critical Data

The three equal roots of eq. 3.4 conform, of course, to the equation

$$(v - x)^3 = v^3 - 3v^2x + 3vx^2 - x^3 = 0$$

where x is the volume at the critical point, v_c, where, also, P becomes P_c and T is T_c. By equating the coefficients of the corresponding powers of v in the two equations, one obtains three simultaneous equations which yield the following relations between the critical constants and the van der Waals parameters:

$$v_c = 3b \qquad P_c = a/27b^2 \qquad T_c = \tfrac{8}{27} a/bR \qquad (3.6)$$

These relations have been chiefly used to obtain values of a and b, since the critical parameters can be easily determined by experiment.

The foregoing relations based upon the van der Waals equation have contributed greatly to the qualitative understanding of the nature of gases and liquids and of the transition from one to the other. In view of the approximate nature of its underlying assumptions, it would be unreasonable to expect it to serve to describe the whole range of gas and liquid $P-V-T$ relations. The molecules are not hard, incompressible spheres: they are more or less soft; they yield more in collisions at higher temperatures than at lower; their intermolecular attractive forces do not fall off with increasing separation in exactly the same way; the cohesion in liquids whose molecules contain a number of atoms does not vary as a/v^2; exponents as high as 2.4 are found for some, as will be reported in Chapter 4.

Some scientists have tried to improve the van der Waals equation by introducing additional variables. Now, almost any inadequate equation can be made to fit the data for one substance better by introducing additional, adjustable parameters, but unless these additions represent independently measurable quantities, an equation so doctored up cannot be expected to predict very well the behavior of a different substance. Polyatomic molecules vary so widely in molecular architecture that no single *equation of state*, such as the van der Waals equation, can be expected to account accurately for the behavior of a variety of substances. It can serve the purpose of a norm, a "reference state," deviations from which are much smaller than they are from the ideal gas law. The practice of expressing actual phenomena in terms of deviations from reference states, or norms, is common and useful.

Corresponding States and Reduced Equations of State

It early became evident that correspondences among the properties of different fluids, whether gases or liquids, should be sought at corresponding temperatures, such as boiling points, instead of at any single temperature. The contribution of van der Waals made critical pressure, temperature, and volume the obvious reference states; therefore two fluids should be most likely to reveal correspondences if compared at equal fractions of their critical pressures, temperatures, and volumes. These fractions are called, respectively, the *reduced pressure, reduced temperature,* and *reduced volume,* expressed symbolically as follows:

$$\pi = P/P_c \qquad \theta = T/T_c \qquad \phi = v/v_c \qquad (3.7)$$

(This π is not the ratio between the circumference and the diameter of a circle.) Since the critical constants are directly measurable, while the parameters of an equation of state, such as the a and b of the van der Waals equation, are not, it is advantageous to obtain a "reduced equation of state" by substituting for P, v, T, A, and b of that equation their corresponding values of π, ϕ, and θ from eqs. 3.7 and of a and b from eqs. 3.6. By straightforward algebra one obtains the van der Waals equation in reduced form:

$$(\pi + 3/\phi^2) \, (3\phi - 1) = 8\theta \qquad (3.8)$$

Plots of π vs. ϕ for different gases at the same value of θ, like P vs. v in Fig. 3.3, agree approximately in the gas region but diverge strongly in the liquid region. Eq. 3.8 possesses, of course, all the shortcomings of the van der Waals equation.

Any substitute for the van der Waals equation, of which there are several, can be put into a reduced form provided it has only three adjustable parameters. More on reduced quantities will be found in Chapter 4.

The Virial Equation of State

A method for expressing deviations from the ideal gas law that is more convenient than the van der Waals equation and is now far more extensively used is the method of the "virial" (Latin *vis*, force). It consists of a series expansion in terms of either volume or pressure:

$$Pv/RT = 1 + B(T)/v + C(T)/v^2 + D(T)/v^3 + \ldots \qquad (3.9)$$

$$Pv/RT = 1 + B'(T)P + C'(T)P^2 + D'(T)P^3 + \cdots \qquad (3.10)$$

The coefficients $B(T)$, etc., are so written in order to indicate that they are functions of temperature. The corresponding coefficients in the two series are related; for example,

$$B' = B/RT \qquad C' = (C - B^2)/RT^2$$

The B and B' terms are called *second virial coefficients;* the C terms are *third virial coefficients*, etc. They are considered to represent the effects of collisions between two or three molecules, respectively. Their relative contributions to the compressibility factor for nitrogen at $0°C$ and several pressures are given in Table 3.1.

TABLE 3.1   Values of Second and Third Virial Coefficients for Nitrogen

P, atm	$B(T)/v$	$C(T)/v^2$
1	-0.0005	$+0.000003$
10	-0.005	$+0.0003$
100	-0.05	$+0.03$

Variations of the compressibility factor with pressure and temperature for several gases are shown in Figs. 3.1 and 3.5.* These variations can be understood qualitatively by reference to the physical significance of the terms of the van der Waals equations, rearranged as follows:

$$Pv + a/v = RT\, v/(v - b) \qquad (3.11)$$

Attractive   Repulsive

The attractive term is, of course, smaller the lower the critical temperature of the gas. It is smallest for He $(T_c =$

*Extensive tables are given in Circular 564 (1955) of the National Bureau of Standards.

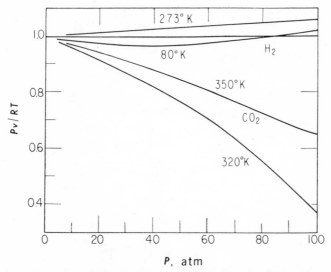

Fig. 3.5 Variation of compressibility factor with pressure and temperature.

5.3° K), a little larger for H_2, followed by Ne, N_2, and O_2 in order. For H_2 at $T = 273°$ K, the effect of the repulsive term predominates; and as P increases, $v/(v - b)$ increases, and therefore Pv/RT rises above 1. However, when T is made very small, 80° K in Fig. 3.5, the attractive term is sufficiently strong below 80 atm to make $Pv/RT < 1$. Its rise at high pressures can be explained by the fact that then $v/(v - b)$ becomes very small. The minimum in the Pv/RT curve is known as the *inversion point* or *Boyle point*.

The shift with temperature is strikingly illustrated for ethylene, C_2H_4, in Fig. 3.6, with Pv/RT plotted against P at 40 and 0° C. At the latter temperature, liquefaction occurs along the vertical line at 40 atm. This line corresponds to the line BEG in Fig. 3.2; it rapidly shortens and disappears at the critical point, where $P = 50.6$ atm, $v = 133$ cm³, and

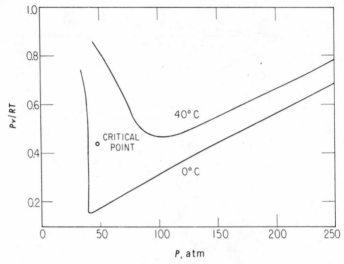

Fig. 3.6 Variations in the compressibility factor for ethylene at 0 and 40° C.

$t = 9.6°$ C. Other gases behave in the same way below their critical points.

Other Equations of State

Other equations of state have been proposed, among them the *Berthelot equation,*

$$Pv = RT + (9R/128) (PT_c/P_c) [1 - 6 (T_c/T^2)] (3.12)$$

which is in the reduced form like eq. 3.8. It is frequently used to calculate the volume of vapors at the boiling point (see Exercise 3).

There are still other equations, with more constants, which can be adjusted empirically to fit experimental data, making them useful for interpolation. However, the use of additional constants does not make an equation more reliable for dealing with a different gas unless these constants can be evaluated from the properties of the pure components.

Pitzer's Acentric Factor

Van der Waals, in 1881, proposed a formula for the vapor pressure of liquids in terms of reduced temperatures and pressures,

$$\log P_c/P = K(T_c/T - 1) \tag{3.13}$$

K is theoretically a universal constant. However, although K is approximately constant for any one substance, as can be seen from the straightness of the lines in Fig. 3.7, it varies from liquid to liquid, increasing with size, complexity, and polarity.

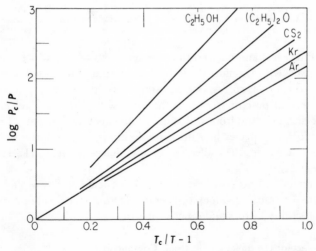

Fig. 3.7 The van der Waals relation between reduced temperature and vapor pressure for five liquids.

Pitzer has recognized departures from the simple, radial type of molecular attraction assumed in the attractive term implied in a/v^2 by introducing an "acentric factor," designated by ω (Greek omega) and defined by

$$\omega = -\log P/P_c - 1.000 \qquad (3.14)$$

where P is the vapor pressure at a reduced temperature of $T/T_c = 0.70$. Liquids with the same ω values may be expected to show the same degree of agreement with the theory of corresponding states. Values of ω for selected fluids are given in Table 3.2.

TABLE 3.2   Values of the "Acentric Factor" (ω)*

Ar	−0.002	C_2H_6	0.105
Xe	+0.002	C_3H_8	0.152
CH_4	0.013	C_6H_6	0.215
N_2	0.040	CO_2	0.225

*K. S. Pitzer, D. Z. Lippman, R. F. Curl, Jr., C. M. Huggins, and D. E. Peterson, *J. Am. Chem. Soc.*, **77**, 3433 (1955); see also G. N. Lewis and M. Randall, "Thermodynamics," revised by K. S. Pitzer and L. Brewer, 2nd ed., McGraw-Hill, New York, 1961.

Pitzer has emphasized that the only substances which can be expected to conform strictly to any formulation based upon the theory of corresponding states are those whose intermolecular potentials vary in the same way with intermolecular distance, and from which quantum effects are absent. The conforming species he calls "simple fluids." The latter condition excludes the molecules of low molecular mass, H_2, He, Ne, CH_4.

Pitzer and his co-workers have constructed extensive tables to assist in using values of acentric factors to calculate compressibility factors and other properties.

Molecular Dynamics by Electronic Computing

B. J. Alder and T. Wainwright* have used a fast electronic computer to study the behavior of molecules moving ran-

Sci. Am., **204**, 113 (Oct. 1959).

domly under specified attractive and repulsive forces at various densities corresponding to the solid, liquid, and gaseous states. Typical results are shown in Figs. 3.8, 3.9, and 3.10. The white lines represent the paths of the centers of molecules. In Fig. 3.8 these move about their average position in the crystal lattice; in Fig. 3.9 the crystal is in the process of melting, and some molecules are escaping from their lattice positions; in Fig. 3.10 thermal agitation is so strong that the lattice structure has completely disappeared, but the molecules still cohere in the completely disordered array of the liquid state, but with "bubbles" of vapor.

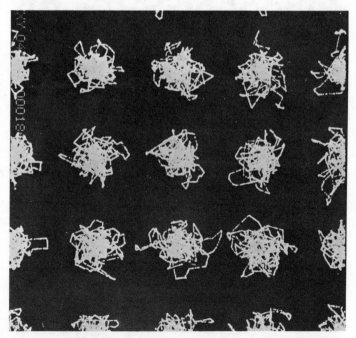

Fig. 3.8 Motions of the centers of molecules of a crystal as calculated by Alder and Wainwright by their "molecular dynamics" procedure.

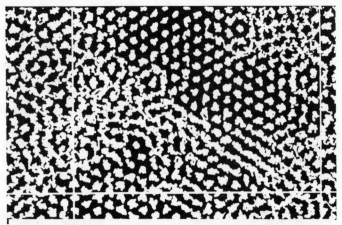

Fig. 3.9 Crystal in process of melting.

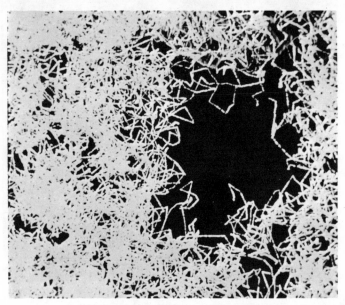

Fig. 3.10 Liquid and its vapor.

The Joule-Thomson Effect

We have thus far considered four cases of gas expansion: (1) the escape of molecules into a vacuum; (2) evolution of a gas against atmospheric pressure, and vice versa; (3) isothermal expansion or compression of a fixed amount of gas at Boyle's law pressure; (4) adiabatic expansion and compression. We now consider a fifth type, the expansion of a gas at a steady higher pressure through a hole or porous plug to a constant lower pressure, as illustrated in principle in Fig. 3.11.

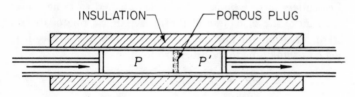

Fig. 3.11 Joule-Thomson expansion.

The pipe in which the plug is placed is insulated so as to prevent heat leak either in or out. Pumps are used to maintain a constant difference in pressure on the two sides of the plug. The pump "upstream," at higher pressure, does the work Pv in forcing a mole of gas through the plug; the one "downstream," the work $P'v'$. We can see from Fig. 3.1 that in the case of hydrogen, $Pv > P'v'$, hence the energy $(Pv - P'v')$ has been introduced into the system, and, since the tube is insulated so that it cannot leak out, it raises the temperature of the gas. But at 80° K, and from 30 atm on down, for hydrogen $Pv > P'v'$, and the temperature must drop.

If $(P_2 - P_1)$ is small, $(T_2 - T_1)$ is, of course, small, and heat leak, in or out, is also small; its effect can be eliminated by extrapolating values of $\Delta T/\Delta P$ to infinitesimal increments, expressed in the symbolism of calculus as $(\partial T/\partial P)_{Ih}$ read as the rate at which temperature changes with the pressure drop when no heat flows in or out of the system. This is called the *Joule-Thomson coefficient*, usually designated by the Greek letter μ (pronounced *mew*). It was first measured by Joule, referred to in Chapter 1, and Thomson, later Lord Kelvin, whose name is attached to the absolute scale of temperature with centigrade degrees.

The reader can easily understand that the magnitude of the change in temperature will be greatest when all of it must appear as translational energy, hence the Joule-Thomson coefficient varies inversely with c_p. To derive the full equation requires a knowledge of thermodynamics. Because many of the readers of this book will not be satisfied to remain ever ignorant of the discipline of thermodynamics, one of the supreme creations of human intelligence, the formula is here given as something to look forward to.

$$\mu = (\partial T/\partial P)_H = (1/c_p) \ [T(\partial V/\partial T)_P - v] \qquad (3.15)$$

The factor $(\partial V/\partial T)_P$ denotes simply the rate of thermal expansion of the particular gas; it is R/P for an ideal gas, for which, therefore, $\mu = 0$.

Gas Thermometry

The precise values of the compressibility factor now available make it possible to determine temperature by measuring the pressure of a fixed amount of gas at constant volume. The precision possible is indicated by the values of the compressibility factor of hydrogen over a range of temperature at pressures of 0.001, 0.1, and 1.0 atm given in Table 3.3.

TABLE 3.3   Compressibility Factor (Pv/RT) for Hydrogen

	Pressure, atm		
T, °K	0.01	0.1	1.0
100	1.0000	1.0000	0.9998
200	1.0000	1.0001	1.0007
300	1.0000	1.0001	1.0006
400	1.0000	1.0000	1.0005

Liquefaction of Gases

Reference was made in Chapter 1 to the fact that before the development of kinetic theory such gases as hydrogen, nitrogen, and oxygen were called "permanent gases," because they had resisted all attempts to liquefy them. As the theory developed, it revealed the fact that the key to liquefaction is not excessively high pressure but temperatures below a certain critical temperature. Thermal pressure must be reduced sufficiently to allow cohesion to hold molecules together as external pressure is lowered. Critical data for several gases are given in Table 3.4. One sees (a) that these critical temperatures, except that for CO_2, are much lower than any temperature attainable during the eighteenth century and (b) that after cooling below a critical temperature, the pressure required will be less than the critical pressure, which is but moderate.

TABLE 3.4   Critical Data

	T_c, °K	P_c, atm	v_c, cm^3
He	5.3	2.26	57
H_2	33.3	12.8	65
N_2	126.1	33.5	90
Ar	150.8	48.0	75
O_2	154.4	74.4	74
CO_2	304.3	72.9	96

There are three ways for attaining temperatures far lower than that which Fahrenheit took as the zero of his scale. One is what may be called the *cascade method*. Its operation may be illustrated with sulfur dioxide, SO_2, ammonia, NH_3, and ethylene, C_2H_4.

The data for SO_2 in Table 3.5 show that it can be liquefied at any temperature below 157°C by applying pressures ranging from 78 atm at 157°C down to 1 atm at −10°C. It is evident that at ordinary temperatures, e.g., 20°C, it could be

TABLE 3.5   Pressure-Temperature Data for Refrigerating Liquids

	P_c, atm	t_c, °C	t_b, °C	t at 100 mm, °C
SO_2	78	157	−10	−48
NH_3	113	132	−33	−67
C_2H_4	51	9.6	−104	−132

liquefied at far less than 78 atm. The exact figure is 3.23 atm.
Ammonia at 20°C has a vapor pressure of 8.46. Both gases,
accordingly, can be easily liquefied by moderate compression.
The heat of condensation is removed by cold water surrounding the condensing coil. If now the pressure over the con-
densed liquid is reduced, the escaping vapor carries off the
heat of evaporation and the temperature of the remaining
liquid is further reduced. If NH_3 is pumped off at 1 atm, the
liquid will be cooled to its boiling point, −33°C; if it is
pumped off at 100 mm pressure, a temperature of −67°C can
be attained. Liquid SO_2, at the same low pressure, can give
−48°C. Both gases are used extensively for refrigeration. For
domestic refrigerators, other gases, called "freons," have been
introduced. Examples are CCl_2F_2, boiling point −29.8°C,
and $CHClF_2$, boiling point −40.8°C. These are chemically
inert and nontoxic.

C_2H_4 can be liquefied by first cooling with liquid NH_3;
then its temperature can be reduced to −132°C at 100 mm.
At 10 mm its temperature would be −153°C, which is below
the critical temperature of oxygen. This cascade effect is not
used by itself to liquefy air, hydrogen, or helium, but is used
to precool before the Joule-Thomson cooling.

A second possible means of lowering the temperature of a
gas sufficiently to achieve liquefaction is to allow it to expand
adiabatically while doing work, an effect discussed in Chapter
2. This method, though theoretically efficient, suffers from a
serious practical difficulty, that of providing lubrication for a
reciprocating engine or a turbine working at very low temperatures.

The third, and most practical, method of liquefying the very low-boiling gases uses Joule-Thomson cooling. To liquefy air, nitrogen, oxygen, etc., the gas must first be compressed, and all water and carbon dioxide removed. The heat of compression is removed with cold water. The compressed gas must then be further cooled by liquid ammonia or ethylene in a heat exchanger, depicted in principle on the right-hand side of Fig. 3.13, to a temperature where, in the Joule-Thomson expansion, P_1v_1 will be considerably less than P_2v_2. The great advantage of strong precooling lies in the considerable decrease of the compressibility factor for nitrogen as temperature is lowered, to be seen in Fig. 3.12.

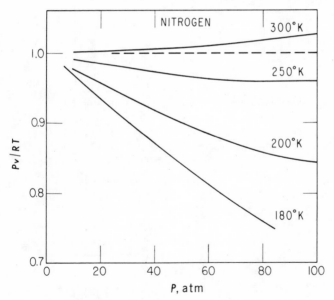

Fig. 3.12 Effect of temperature upon the compressibility factor of nitrogen.

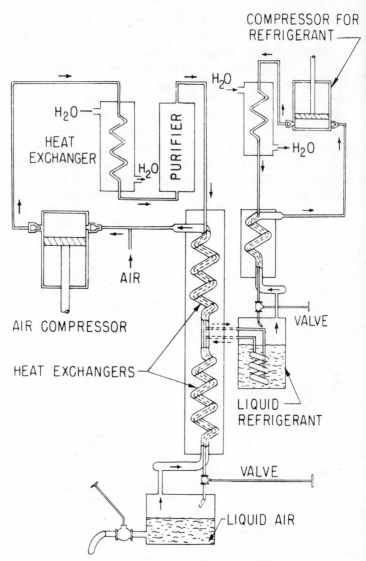

Fig. 3.13 Schematic diagram of apparatus for liquefying air.

The next step is Joule-Thomson expansion through an adjustable valve, as illustrated schematically in Fig. 3.13. When the flow begins, there is a lot of metal apparatus to be cooled. The gas that comes through the valve at the bottom of the figure to the low-pressure side flows back over the pipe containing the compressed gas, taking heat from the latter. Compressed gas thus arrives at the valve at progressively lower and lower temperatures. When the temperature is sufficiently low, further Joule-Thomson cooling causes some of the gas to liquefy. That portion which does not liquefy is added to the incoming gas, and all is compressed, cooled, and re-expanded in the liquefier.

It is possible, in the course of liquefying air, to obtain liquid oxygen and nitrogen separately because of the difference, 12.7°, in their boiling points (90.1 and 77.4°K, respectively). Since liquid oxygen, despite its low boiling temperature at 1 atm, is very concentrated, it strongly supports combustion. Powdered charcoal, wet with the right amount of liquid oxygen, is a powerful explosive. Liquid nitrogen is therefore preferred to liquid air for low-temperature laboratory research for the sake of safety.

Transport Phenomena: Heat Conductivity, Viscosity, and Diffusion

Kinetic theory has been successfully applied in the analysis of certain important, related phenomena having to do with the rates at which they proceed. These include heat conductivity, viscosity, and diffusion. Conductivity of a gas for heat is the rate at which the gas transports heat from a surface at a higher temperature to one at a lower temperature. The *specific conductivity*, κ (Greek kappa), of a gas is the amount of heat that it transports from 1 cm² of one surface at $T°$ to 1 cm² of another parallel to it 1 cm distant and at $(T - 1)°$.

Specific viscosity, denoted by η (Greek eta), is the resistance offered by the gas to the parallel movement of one surface with respect to another at a velocity of 1 cm sec^{-1} per square centimeter of surface. In this case it is molecular momentum that is transported from one surface to another.

Viscosity is usually determined in practice from the volume of gas, V, that flows per second through a tube of length L and radius R from pressure P_1 to P_2. The formula is

$$\eta = \pi(P_1^2 - P_2^2)R^4/16LP_0V \qquad (3.16)$$

Here P_0 is $\frac{1}{2}(P_1 - P_2)$.

The diffusion coefficient of a gas is, similarly, the amount in grams that diffuses through a gas having the same parameters, such as its isotope, per centimeter per second per square centimeter.

These are all called "*transport processes.*" In the first, what is transported is heat; in the second, momentum; in the third, matter. It is surely evident that the rate of each process depends upon the mean molecular velocity, $\bar{u}$, and upon the mean distance that each molecule travels between collisions, λ (Greek lambda). In the case of diffusion, the relation is extremely simple,

$$D = \tfrac{1}{3}\bar{u}\lambda \qquad (3.17)$$

The detailed analysis of the problem required to derive the coefficient $\frac{1}{3}$ lies beyond the proper scope of this book. An "introduction" to calculating $\bar{u}$ for a given gas at a stated temperature was developed in Chapter 2. Methods for determining λ are to be discussed later.

The viscosity depends upon the average momentum of diffusing molecules, introduced by adding the mass density, $\rho = mn$, where n, as earlier, is the number of molecules per cubic centimeter. The relation is thus

$$\eta = \rho D = \tfrac{1}{3}\rho\bar{u}\lambda \qquad (3.18)$$

Thermal conductivity, κ, simply multiplies the viscosity by the factor, c_v, the specific heat *per gram*, giving

$$\kappa = c_v \eta = \tfrac{1}{3}\rho c_v \bar{u} \lambda \tag{3.19}$$

These three properties, D, η, and κ, are all directly measurable, viscosity most easily; and either D or κ can be calculated from η simply by eliminating λ.

Mean Free Path

The mean distance, λ, traveled by a molecule between collisions must depend, one can easily see, upon n, the number of molecules per cubic centimeter, and upon the sizes of the molecules. Denoting its diameter by the usual symbol, σ (Greek sigma), let us imagine a molecule, A (Fig. 3.14), moving from left to right. It will collide with no molecule whose center is distant by more than the distance σ from the line traced out by the center of A. Between collisions, therefore, no other molecule is encountered within an imaginary cylinder whose cross section is $\pi\sigma^2$, whose length, on the average,

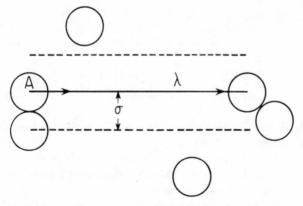

Fig. 3.14 Illustration of the mean free path of a molecule.

is λ, and whose volume is therefore $\pi\sigma^2\lambda$. At each collision molecule A is diverted into a new path and traces a new but similar exclusion cylinder. After n collisions, it will have traced out a total exclusion volume of $\pi n\sigma^2\lambda = 1$ cm³.

A factor, $\sqrt{2}$ (= 1.41), is introduced to take account of the exchanges of momentum between colliding molecules. The justification of this lies beyond the scope of this little volume. The final equation is then

$$\lambda = 1/\sqrt{2}\pi n\sigma^2 \tag{3.20}$$

This expression for λ can be substituted into any of the three equations 3.17, 3.18, and 3.19. In 3.18, for example, it gives

$$\eta = m\bar{u}/\tfrac{1}{3}\sqrt{2}\pi\sigma^2 \tag{3.21}$$

Since η is accurately measurable, this equation offers one of the best methods for calculating σ. Illustrative values are given in Table 3.6. The values are expressed in Ångstrom units (1 Å = 10^{-8} cm). This unit is very appropriate for expressing atomic and molecular dimensions.

TABLE 3.6.   Molecular Diameter (σ)
(In Ångstrom units, 10^{-8} cm)

He	2.6	O_2	3.5
H_2	2.9	N_2	3.7
Ar	3.4	CH_4	3.8
Xe	4.1	Cl_2	4.2

In order to appreciate the magnitudes involved, let us make two calculations. First, what is the mean free path of nitrogen molecules when the gas is at 0°C and 1 atm? Because values of σ are good to no more than two significant figures, the result is not significant beyond two figures.

We must use the same units for all quantities involved. If we were to use 3.7 Å for σ, we would have to express n as the number of molecules per cubic Ångstrom, which is 10^{-24} cm³. The figure for λ would then be in Ångstroms. Let us, however, stick to the c.g.s. system, where $\sigma = 3.7 \times 10^{-8}$ cm. and $\sigma^2 = 13.7 \times 10^{-16}$ cm².

As for n, since there are 6.0×10^{23} molecules in 2.24×10^3 cm³, $n = 2.7 \times 10^{19}$ molecules cm⁻³. (n, by the way, is often called the Loschmidt number.)

Equation 3.20 then gives

$$\lambda = \frac{1}{1.4 \times 3.14 \times 2.7 \times 10^{19} \times 13.7 \times 10^{-16}}$$

$$= 6.1 \times 10^{-6} \text{ cm}$$

Since $\sigma = 3.7 \times 10^{-8}$ cm, $\lambda/\sigma = 165$; that is, *the mean free path of nitrogen molecules is 165 times their diameter*. This figure helps to explain why nitrogen at 0°C and 1 atm behaves so nearly like an ideal gas.

Let us calculate, next, the pressure, in millimeters of mercury, at which the mean free path would be 1 cm.

With $\lambda = 1$ cm, $n = 1/4.46\sigma^2 = 1.6 \times 10^{14}$ molecules cm⁻³. We found, above, that when $P = 760$ mm, $n = 2.7 \times 10^{19}$ molecules cm⁻³; therefore, in this case

$$P = 760(1.6 \times 10^{14})/(2.7 \times 10^{19}) = 4.5 \times 10^{-3} \text{ mm}$$

With modern methods of producing high vacuum, much lower pressures than this can be attained, greatly lengthening the mean free paths required for experiments with long, parallel beams of molecules.

Having obtained the figure for the pressure of nitrogen that would give a mean free path of 1 cm, we can quickly calculate the mean free path of hydrogen at the same pressure. It would obviously be greater in the ratio of $(3.7/2.9)^2$, or 1.6 cm.

Comparisons between the thermal conductivities of different gases are interesting. Table 3.7 gives sample values. Hydrogen heads the list. Since its molecular weight is only one half that of helium, its molecules have the highest velocity; its heat capacity is higher than that of helium because its molecules are diatomic. These advantages as a conductor of heat are only partly offset by its shorter mean free path by reason of its larger diameter.

TABLE 3.7. Thermal Conductivity of Gases
(In cal cm^{-1} sec^{-1} deg^{-1})

H_2	400	C_2H_4	41
He	330	Ar	39
CH_4	72	CO_2	36
O_2	58	Cl_2	18

Methane, CH_4, has a higher conductivity than any of the gases below it in the table by reason of its low molecular weight and consequent high molecular velocity. Chlorine, with the smallest $\bar{u}$ and largest σ, has by far the smallest thermal conductivity.

The extraordinarily high heat conductivity of helium, second only to hydrogen, was a disadvantage that had to be overcome when helium–oxygen mixtures were adopted for deep diving in place of compressed air. The thermal conductivity of helium is roughly seven times that of nitrogen; consequently, heat is transported so rapidly from the body of the diver to the water that no ordinary clothing sufficed to keep him warm. It was necessary to devise an electrically heated suit and, moreover, to construct it of noncombustible material because of the considerable partial pressure of the oxygen in the mixture.

Argon and carbon dioxide have nearly the same molecular weights, 39.9 and 44, and therefore nearly the same molecular velocities; CO_2, because of its triatomic molecules, has a much greater heat capacity, 6.75 vs. 3.0 cal $mole^{-1}$ deg^{-1}, but this is largely offset by its much smaller mean free path, 400 vs. 635 Å.

Intermolecular Forces

We have said that the van der Waals term a/v^2 is no more than an approximate way of taking account of intermolecular attractions. The corresponding term in the thermodynamic equation of state, $(\partial E/\partial V)_T$, provides a precise measure, but we would need to know how it varies with V and T. The second virial coefficient, $B(T)$ in eq. 3.9, is still another experimental measure. It can be related to a function $\phi(r)$, which is the potential energy between a pair of molecules as it varies with the distance, r, between their centers. The equation is

$$B(T) = -2\pi N_0 \int_0^\infty \left\{\exp\left[-\phi(r)/\mathbf{k}T\right] - 1\right\} r^2 dr \qquad (3.22)$$

(The symbol $\mathbf{k}$ here is the Boltzmann constant, not to be confused with the attraction constant, k, in eq. 3.23 below.)

The form adopted for $\phi(r)$ must express the fact that the attraction at larger distances changes to repulsion at smaller distances as illustrated in Fig. 3.15. This has been accomplished by writing

$$\phi(r) = \mathrm{j}/r^n - \mathrm{k}/r^6 \qquad (3.23)$$

The term k/r^6 is the attractive term. The 6th power of r comes from an analysis by F. London, published in 1930, of a theory of the interaction of two electron systems. The term j/r^n represents the repulsion that occurs at small distances. The exponent n is often set at 12; this simplifies calculations and makes it possible to reproduce the P–V–T data for simple gases rather well by selecting values for j and k that give the best fit.

Instead of j and k, one may use the parameters σ and ϵ, the

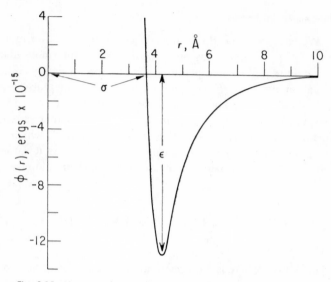

Fig. 3.15   Variation of intermolecular pair potential with distance between molecular centers.

"depth of the potential well" in Fig. 3.15. When $\phi(r) = 0$, $r = \sigma$, and when $d\phi(r)/dr = 0$, $\phi(r) = \epsilon$, whence $j = k\sigma^6$ and $k = 4\epsilon\sigma^6$. Eq. 3.23 thus becomes

$$\phi(r) = 4\epsilon[(\sigma/r)^{12} - (\sigma/r)^6] \qquad (3.24)$$

If the factor within brackets is written in reduced form as $f(\sigma/r)$, the second virial coefficient can also be expressed in reduced form,

$$B(T) = \sigma^3\Phi(\mathbf{k}T/\epsilon) \qquad (3.25)$$

The form of the function Φ depends upon the form of the function f. In this way, values of both σ and ϵ can be determined from Joule-Thomson coefficients. The values of σ so derived agree only moderately well with those obtained from viscosity. This is not to be wondered at, since (1) values of σ and ϵ are adjusted together differently to fit data by different observers and (2) the various gases do not conform strictly to the assumptions made in the theoretical treatment. The polyatomic molecules especially have different degrees of softness, and intermolecular forces do not necessarily vary with an inverse power of the distance between their centers. Table 3.8 gives samples of the values of σ and of ϵ/k, where k is the Boltzmann constant. The degree of experimental uncertainty is shown by spread in the figures for the same quantity.

TABLE 3.8 Values of σ and ϵ/k Obtained from Viscosity and Second Virial Coefficient

	From $B(T)$		From viscosity	
	σ, Å	ϵ/k, °K	σ, Å	ϵ/k, °K
Ar	3.405	124	3.42	124
	3.40	116	3.47	116
CO_2	4.49	189	4.00	190
	4.07	205	3.90	213

Gas Mixtures

We have seen that air has been treated successfully as if it were a single species; only when both liquid and gas are present is it necessary to consider it as a mixture. In general, however, it is desirable to predict the properties of mixtures from those of the pure components. The compressibility factors of mixtures clearly involve three separate interactions; for a two-component mixture we may designate them as 1–1, 2–2, and 1–2. The last, those between pairs of different species, we must, of course, be able to calculate in terms of the interactions between pairs of the same species.

Van der Waals proposed that the attractive constant for a mixture of gases should have the following form,

$$a = a_1 x_1^2 + 2a_{12} x_1 x_2 + a_2 x_2^2 \qquad (3.26)$$

where x_1 and x_2 are the mole fractions of the respective species.

He suggested the same functional form for the b of the mixture, but a simpler form has proven more satisfactory,

$$b_{12} = \tfrac{1}{2}(b_1 + b_2) \tag{3.27}$$

Berthelot proposed that the interaction constant between the unlike species be calculated as the geometrical mean of the constants for the pure components

$$a_{12} = (a_{11}a_{22})^{1/2} \tag{3.28}$$

The second virial coefficient, B, for a mixture has been formulated like eqs. 3.26 and 3.28, and the σ values in mixtures have been commonly expressed, like eq. 3.27, as arithmetical means.

All such assumptions, whether applied to these or to other equations of state, agree only moderately well with experiment, except for mixtures of the simplest molecules. The weakest point in the argument is probably the geometric mean assumption, except in mixtures of molecular species that closely resemble each other, such as N_2 and CO. These discrepancies are more clearly revealed by liquid mixtures, for which significant data are much more easily obtained, than for gas mixtures, where determination of virial coefficients is difficult and tedious. Evidence from liquid mixtures is presented in Chapter 4.

Exercises

1. Why does the mean free path depend upon σ^2 instead of σ?
2. What simplifications are involved in the van der Waals equation that limit its applicability through long ranges of pressure and temperature?
3. D. Berthelot, in 1907, proposed as an equation of state,

$$Pv = RT + (9R/128)(PT_c/P_c)[1 - 6(T_c/T)^2]$$

Carbon tetrachloride boils at $350°K$. Its $P_c = 45.0$ atm, $T_c = 556°K$. How does v so calculated differ from the volume it would occupy as an ideal gas?

Ans. Writing the equation

$$v = RT/P + (9R/128)(T_c/P_c)[1 - 6(T_c/T)^2]$$

We see that the difference called for is

$$\Delta v = v - RT/P + (9R/128)(T_c/P_c)(1 - 6(T_c/T)^2]$$

Expressing P in atmospheres and taking R as 82.1 cm³ atm mole⁻¹ deg⁻¹, we obtain $\Delta v = -1000$ cm³.

Note that the right-hand member of the above equation is in the form of a second virial coefficient.

4. Taking the diameter of a helium atom-molecule as 2.6Å, calculate its mean free path in the gas of 0°C and 1 atm.

Ans. This of course involves n, the number of molecules per cubic centimeter. Since there are 6.0×10^{23} molecules per mole in 2.24×10^4 cm³ at 0°C and 1 atm, $n = 2.69 \times 10^{19}$ molecules cm⁻³ ($1 = 10^8$ Å). We must use the same units for n and σ, so we write $\sigma = 2.6$ Å $= 2.6 \times 10^{-8}$ cm and $\sigma^2 = 5.56 \times 10^{-16}$ cm². Substituting in eq. 3.20 gives

$$\lambda = \frac{1}{1.415 \times 3.14 \times 2.69 \times 10^{19} \times 5.56 \times 10^{-16}}$$

$$= \frac{1}{6.65 \times 10^4} = 1.5 \times 10^{-5} \text{ cm}$$

or, if you please, 1500Å (580 times σ).

5. From the answer to 4 and the molecular weight of He = 4.0 calculate the number of collisions per second of a helium molecule.

6. How many molecules of gas per cubic centimeter are there in an x-ray tube evacuated to a pressure of 10^{-5} mm at 20°C?

7. The value of Pv/RT for H_2 at 200 atm and 20°C is 1.206. What balloon capacity could be filled by the hydrogen contained in a steel "bottle" of 1.00 ft³ capacity at 200 atm and 20°C?

8. In deriving the number 28.8 for the weight of 22.41 liters of dry air at 0°C and 1 atm, the presence of argon was neglected, and the fraction of O_2 molecules was taken roughly as $\frac{1}{5}$. Calculate a more accurate value from the following figures: 78% N_2, 21% O_2, 1% A.

9. What effect does water vapor have upon the density of air?

10. How does the humidity of air affect its heat conductivity? Explain.

11. From the following experimentally determined values for the critical point of CO_2—$T_c = 304°K$, $P_c = 73$ atm, $v_c = 96$ cm^3—calculate the corresponding values of the van der Waals a and b. Using these parameters, plot Pv vs. P for (a) 17°C and (b) 47°C.

chapter four

LIQUIDS, SOLIDS, AND SOLUTIONS

The Transition of Gas to Liquid

THE FAMILIAR, practical distinction between a gas and a liquid is that a gas expands to fill its container while a liquid has a self-limiting volume. If a gas below its critical temperature is gradually compressed at constant temperature, a saturation point is reached beyond which, as the volume is further reduced, liquid begins to form in the lower part of the vessel and continues to increase, the pressure remaining constant, until all the gas disappears. Further compression of the liquid requires great increases in pressure.

We saw in Chapter 3, however, that it is possible to go continuously from gas to liquid by raising the temperature of the gas above its critical value, compressing to a volume less than the critical volume, and then cooling below the critical temperature; at no point in this indirect path has anything occurred to indicate transition from gas to liquid. There is no reason to regard the structure at the low temperature and pressure at the end of the trip as significantly different from what it was at the beginning.

Let us again interpret conditions in terms of the two equations of state, thermodynamic and van der Waals, given in Chapter 3 (eqs. 3.3 and 3.4).

$$P + (\partial E/\partial V)_T = T(\partial P/\partial T)_V \qquad (4.1)$$

$$P \quad + \quad a/v^2 \quad = TR/(v - b) \tag{4.2}$$

Pressures: External   Attractive   Thermal

Above the critical temperature, thermal pressure so far exceeds attractive pressure as to require large external pressure to reduce the fluid to the volume of a liquid. If this pressure is decreased isothermally, the whole expands into gas. (The reader may wish to trace these changes in Fig. 3.1.)

When temperature is decreased to an extent sufficient to reduce thermal pressure to nearly the magnitude of the attractive pressure at the volume of the liquid state, then very little external pressure suffices to prevent expansion into vapor.

During a gradual transition from gas to liquid by the above roundabout path, the main changes are connected with the fact that at low gas concentrations most of the interaction causing deviation from ideal gas behavior occurs during collisions between pairs of molecules, that is, binary collisions. The probability of three molecules colliding simultaneously in a gas at low pressure is very small indeed compared with that of binary collision. The van der Waals term a/v^2 and the second virial term $B(T)/v^2$ account rather well for low pressure compressibility coefficients. But as molecules become more and more closely crowded together, a single molecule acquires a number of near neighbors at distances between σ and 2σ. The number varies in liquids from about seven to ten, depending upon the temperature.

Figure 4.1 shows the average number of atoms of sodium around a central atom at various distances, calculated from the scattering of X-rays by liquid sodium at $100°$ C, just above its melting point. The plot shows about nine nearest neighbors. In a curve obtained for sodium at $400°$ C, the peak height corresponds to seven nearest neighbors.

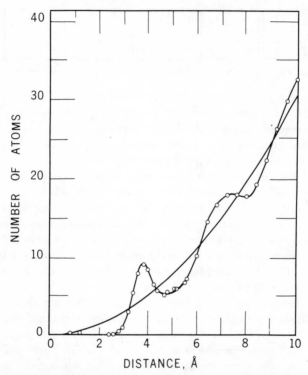

Fig. 4.1 The average number of sodium atoms at varying distance around a central atom, calculated from X-ray scattering at 100° C.

The Transition between Liquid and Crystalline Solid

The transition between liquid and crystalline solid, on the other hand, is quite abrupt. In a crystal the molecules are arranged in a regular lattice; in liquids, other than water and certain others containing hydrogen bonds, the molecules are in a state of maximum disorder. The molecules in a single plane of a crystal may be compared to people seated in an auditorium; while those in a liquid resemble people milling

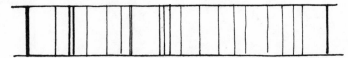

Fig. 4.2 The line structure of X-ray scattering by solid gallium at 22° C.

about in a dense crowd. X-rays scattered by solid gallium at 22° C gave lines at different wavelengths, corresponding to the regular spacing of the atoms, as illustrated in Fig. 4.2. In liquid gallium at 30.5° C only a few broad bands were found, in regions having no simple relation to the lines.

A number of scientists have tried to deal with the P–V–T energy relations of liquids by assuming that liquids have a sort of mussed-up lattice structure, with holes here and there, as in crystal lattices. This makes calculations simpler, because one knows the distances between all the molecules of a solid, while in a liquid one knows only the average distance and the number of nearest neighbors; these distances rapidly become blurred at distances beyond 2σ.

There are certain behaviors of liquids that are quite inconsistent with lattice structure. Especially striking evidence is offered by the fact that many liquids which are composed of very simple, symmetrical molecules can survive supercooling far below their melting points. Phosphorus, whose molecules, P_4, are regular tetrahedra, and which melts at 44° C, can remain liquid indefinitely at room temperatures, some 20° lower, and small drops of it have been cooled to $-70°$ C without crystallizing. If any lattice structures were present in the liquid, it is difficult to understand why they would not grow under such drastic cooling.

Even more striking evidence is offered by the effect of temperature on two isomers, m-xylene and p-xylene. These differ merely in the positions of their two —CH_3 groups. Their structures are represented in Fig. 4.3. The molecules of both are flat, all carbon atoms lying in the same plane. Those of

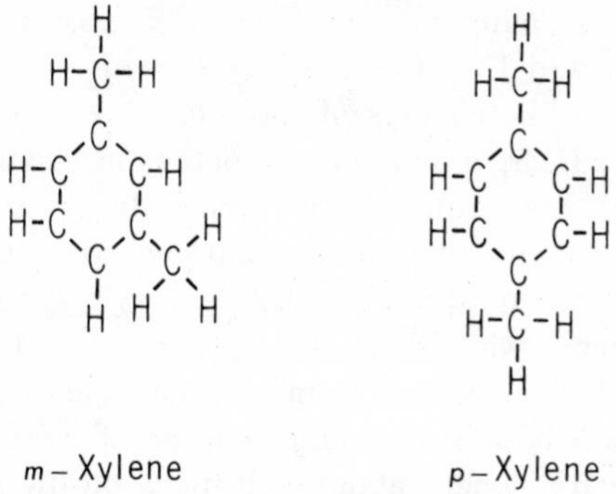

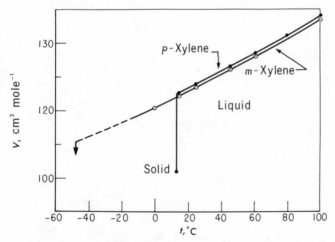

Fig. 4.3 The molecular structures of *m*- and *p*-xylenes.

p-xylene, as might be inferred from their shape, pack more tightly into a crystal lattice; the freezing point of *p*-xylene is 13.2°C; that of *m*-xylene is −47.9°C. Their boiling points differ by only 0.8°C. Fig. 4.4 shows how their volumes per

Fig. 4.4 Comparison of molal volumes of *m*-xylene and *p*-xylene.

mole vary with temperature.   They differ by only 0.5 cm³
between 100 and 13.2°C. It seems obvious that if any in-
cipient crystal-like clusters of molecules were present they
would be much larger and more numerous in *p*-xylene than in
m-xylene, causing a considerable drop in the molal volume of
the former as its melting point is approached. One sees that
no such decrease occurs; evidently the *p*-xylene even at 15°C
does not "know" what is about to happen to it at 13.2°C.

It seems that one should think of crystals as regular arrays
of molecules, whose heat motions consist of oscillations with
recognizable frequencies about their mean positions. As temperature rises from near to 0°K, these vibrations absorb energy in definite amounts called *quanta*. A plot of heat content

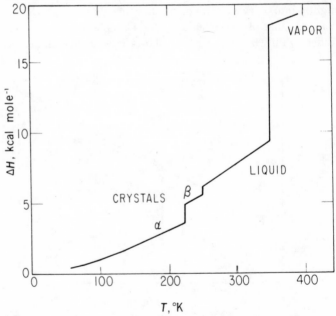

Fig. 4.5 Temperature variation of the heat content per mole of carbon tetrachloride. α and β designate two different crystal forms.

vs. temperature for CCl_4 is shown in Fig. 4.5. Tangents to these curves at any temperature, their "slopes," indicate heat capacities at these points. In the symbolism of calculus, $(\partial H/\partial T)_P = c_P$.

The molecules of liquids are not vibrating about fixed positions, each is milling about with its immediate neighbors in purely random fashion; in terms of frequency, there is "noise," but no "tone."

Energy-Volume Relations in Liquids

If a liquid is compressed or expanded in a thermostat, its energy does not vary inversely with the square of the volume, as does that of a dilute gas, but with some other, that is, $1/v^n$, where n has a characteristic value for each liquid. Values of $(\partial E/\partial V)_T$ can be obtained with high accuracy from measurements of $(\partial P/\partial T)_V$. The volume of a liquid confined in a glass vessel over mercury can be held constant at a series of temperatures and the pressure measured at each temperature. It has been found that the relation between P and T is a straight line for each value of volume over a range of as much as 200 atm. Table 4.1 gives values of $(\partial P/\partial T)_V$ for several liquids at different molal volumes. From these, values of $(\partial E/\partial V)_T$ have been calculated by eq. 4.1. Their variation with volume can be expressed throughout the ranges measured by substituting in eq. 4.2 a variable, x, as the exponent of v, giving:

$$(\partial E/\partial V)_T = a/v^x \qquad (4.3)$$

TABLE 4.1 Values of $(\partial P/\partial T)_V$ and of $(\partial E/\partial V)_T$ at 25°C

Liquid	$v,$ cm^3 mole^{-1}	$(\partial P/\partial T)_V,$ atm deg^{-1}	$(\partial E/\partial V)_T,$ atm	n
CS_2	60.6	12.31	3670	1.89
CCl_4	97.1	11.22	3340	2.09
$CCl_2F \cdot CClF_2$	62.6	8.67	2585	2.19
c-$Si_4O_4(CH_3)_8$	312.0	7.88	2350	2.30
c-$C_6F_{11}CF_3$	195.7	7.53	2245	2.44

One sees that values of x vary from about 1.9 to as much as 2.44. This is one reason for the failure of the van der Waals equation to account for the liquid region by parameters obtained in the region of gas or at the critical point.

The last two liquids listed in Table 4.1 have very large molecules. The octamethylcyclotetrasiloxane molecule is exceptionally huge. Its core, Si_4O_4, is buried under eight methyl (CH_3) groups. The cohesion or internal pressure of the liquid results mainly from the attraction between these groups; the central core contributes very little; consequently, this attraction should be formulated in terms, not of distance between the centers of two molecules, but rather of the distance between contiguous methyl groups. Instead of expressing attractive potential by a term such as k/r^6, a term such as $k'/(r - a)^6$ seems more appropriate. This is called a "Kihara potential," after the man who proposed it.

Solubility Parameters and Force Constants

Information about intermolecular forces is experimentally much more easily obtained from liquids and liquid mixtures than from gases and gas mixtures because, as illustrated in Table 4.1, the attractive forces in liquids are of the order of several thousand atmospheres, while in gases they are very small. The *energy* of cohesion, called the *cohesive energy density*, is directly measured by the energy of vaporization per cubic centimeter of liquid, $\Delta E^{vap}/V$. Our best formulation for liquid mixtures involves the square root of the cohesive energy density; this parameter has been given the name *solubility parameter*, with the symbol δ (Greek delta). The relation is

$$\delta = (\Delta E^{vap}/V)^{1/2} \tag{4.4}$$

Values of δ for representative nonpolar liquids are given in Table 4.2. The energy of vaporization is obtained from the

TABLE 4.2   Values of the Solubility Parameter (δ) at 25° C

C_7F_{16}	Perfluoroheptane	5.9
$c\text{-}C_6F_{11}CF_3$	Perfluoromethylcyclohexane	6.0
$c\text{-}C_4Cl_2F_6$	Dichlorohexafluorocyclobutane	7.1
$CCl_2F \cdot CClF_2$	Trichlorotrifluoroethane	7.3
$SiCl_4$	Silicon tetrachloride	7.5
$c\text{-}C_6H_{12}$	Cyclohexane	8.2
CCl_4	Carbon tetrachloride	8.6
$TiCl_4$	Titanium tetrachloride	9.0
C_6H_6	Benzene	9.2
$CHCl_3$	Chloroform	9.3
CS_2	Carbon disulfide	10.0
$CHBr_3$	Bromoform	10.5
Br_2	Bromine	11.5

heat of vaporization by subtracting the work done against the atmosphere, $Pv = RT$, as explained in Chapter 2.

The energy required to vaporize 1 cm³ of a liquid is closely related to the energy required to separate two molecules, formulated in eqs. 3.23 and 3.24, since vaporization involves overcoming the forces between all the molecules in 1 cm³ of liquid. There is no need to burden the reader at this stage of his education with the quantitative details of the derivation; we simply show, in Table 4.3, that there exists a close parallel between the solubility parameters of liquids and the "force constants," $\epsilon/\mathbf{k}$, between pairs of molecules, illustrated in Table 3.8. The values of $\epsilon/\mathbf{k}$ in Table 4.3 are those determined from viscosity of vapors.

TABLE 4.3   Parallel between Solubility Parameters (δ) of Liquids and the Force Constants for Pairs of Molecules in Vapor, Derived from Viscosity

Substance	δ (liquid)	$\epsilon/\mathbf{k}$ (vapor)
C_6H_{12}	8.2	324
CCl_4	8.6	327
C_6H_6	9.2	440
CS_2	10.0	488
Br_2	11.5	520

Liquid Mixtures

Let us imagine a pure liquid in equilibrium with its vapor, as depicted in Fig. 4.6A. The vapor pressure of the pure liquid is $P_1{}^\circ$. Let us imagine, now, that $\frac{1}{5}$ of the "white" molecules have been replaced by "black" molecules of another species, but similar in size and intermolecular forces (Fig. 4.6B). We might use δ values as our guide. The first two liquids in Table 4.2 would come very close to meeting the specification.

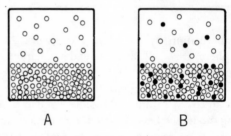

Fig. 4.6   Kinetic basis of Raoult's law.

Now a "white" molecule, since it is blind, does not know that anything has happened; it feels itself subject to the same forces as before, and has the same tendency to escape from the liquid and the same tendency to re-enter it. The only difference is that now only $\frac{4}{5}$ of the molecules are "white," in both the liquid and vapor phases. The *partial* pressure of "white" molecules, P_1, is now $\frac{4}{5} P_1{}^\circ$. If all the molecules were "black," their vapor pressure would be $P_2{}^\circ$, so in the mixture they contribute a partial pressure, P_2, equal to $\frac{1}{5} P_0$.

In general, if the mole fractions of the two species in such a mixture are x_1 and x_2, respectively, then

$$P_1 = P_1{}^\circ x_1 \qquad P_2 = P_2{}^\circ x_2 \qquad (4.5)$$

and the total pressure,

$$P = P_1 + P_2 = P_1{}^{\circ}x_1 + P_2{}^{\circ}x_2 \qquad (4.6)$$

Equation 4.5 is *Raoult's law*. Note that eq. 4.6 is for liquid mixtures the equivalent of Dalton's law (cf. Chapter 2) for gas mixtures. Moreover, it can be seen, by comparing the foregoing with the discussion of gas mixtures in Chapter 3, that near equality of δ values for components of liquid mixture and of $\epsilon/\mathbf{k}$ values for gas mixtures both lead to reasonably good prediction of the properties of mixtures from those of their pure components.

But what about components whose solubility parameters differ considerably? Here we encounter, as with gas mixtures, the consequences of the approximate geometrical mean of the attractive potentials of the pure components. With gases it was the Berthelot mean, eq. 3.28; with liquids it is

$$\delta_1\delta_2 = [(\Delta E_1{}^{\text{vap}}/V_1)\,(\Delta E_2{}^{\text{vap}}/V_2)]^{1/2} \qquad (4.7)$$

If $(x_1 + x_2)$ moles of mixture are formed by evaporating the proper amounts of the pure components, mixing the vapors, and condensing to the mixture, the net energy of the process, the energy of mixing, involves the difference between the sum of the 1–1 and the 2–2 potential energies lost and the 1–2 energies that replace them:

$$\Delta E_{11}{}^{\text{vap}}/V_1 + \Delta E_{22}{}^{\text{vap}}/V_2 - 2\Delta E_{12}/V_{12}$$

If the geometric mean holds for the 1–2 interaction, this becomes a perfect square, and the energy of mixing is

$$\Delta E^{\text{M}} = (x_1 v_1 + x_2 v_2)(\delta_1 - \delta_2)^2 \phi_1 \phi_2 \qquad (4.8)$$

Here the ϕ's are the volume fractions of the respective components,

$$\phi_1 = \frac{x_1 v_1}{x_1 v_1 + x_2 v_2} \qquad \phi_2 = \frac{x_2 v_2}{x_1 v_1 + x_2 v_2} \qquad (4.9)$$

For the derivation of eq. 4.8 it was necessary to assume, in accord with the evidence cited earlier, that the molecules in the mixture are in a state of maximum disorder. Kinetic theory has played a key role in developing a theory of mixtures.

Now, as the reader was reminded in Chapter 3, a geometrical mean is less than an arithmetical mean, as may be easily tested by trial; for example, $(4 \times 9)^{1/2} = 6; \frac{1}{2}(4 + 9) = 6.5$. Consequently, *the mixing of two liquids with different δ values is accompanied by a weakening of cohesion, resulting in expansion, absorption of heat, and greater vapor pressures than those calculated by Raoult's law.*

If their δ values differ sufficiently, the two components resist complete mixing, giving curves for mole fraction or volume fraction vs. temperature such as those in Fig. 4.7. The critical mixing temperature rises with increasing difference between solubility parameters of the components, modified, according to theory, by the magnitude of molal volumes.

Regular Solutions

If one component is a solid, its vapor pressure is less than it would be if it were liquid in a ratio dependent upon its melting point and heat of fusion, because its vapor pressure, P_2^s (designating it as component 2), is less than what it would be in the state of a supercooled liquid. If it obeys Raoult's law, its solubility, x_2^i, would be given by $P_2^s = P_2^\circ x_2^i$. The ratio P_2^s / P_2° is called the *activity* of the solid, a_2^s. If, as is usually the case, it does not obey Raoult's law, $a_2^s > x_2^i$ by an amount that depends upon the energy or heat of mixing. The formula for the solubility of a solid derived from an analysis of these considerations is

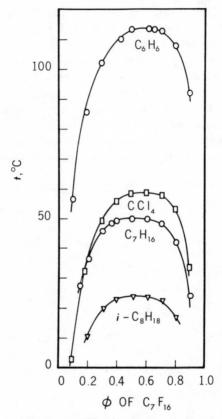

Fig. 4.7 Liquid-liquid solubility of binary mixtures of perfluoroheptane, C_7F_{16}.

$$\ln x_2^2 = \ln a_2^s - v_2\phi_1^2(\delta_2 - \delta_1)^2/RT \qquad (4.10)$$

This can be expected to apply reasonably well only when selective chemical interactions are absent. Only when the interactions are purely physical is thermal agitation able to mix the component molecules in the state of maximum disorder, or randomness, necessary for deriving eq. 4.8. Solutions behaving with such regularity that eq. 4.8 is applicable are called *regular solutions*. The regularity is illustrated in Fig. 4.8, where the solubility of iodine is plotted in a series of solvents in the form $\log_{10} x_2^s$ vs. $\log T$. We see a regular family of lines whose spread and slopes are determined by v_2 and $(\delta_2 - \delta_1)^2$. The slopes of the lines give the *entropy* of solution, which has its maximum value in a regular, completely disordered mixture. These solutions have the same violet color as iodine vapor. The dashed lines are for solutions that are

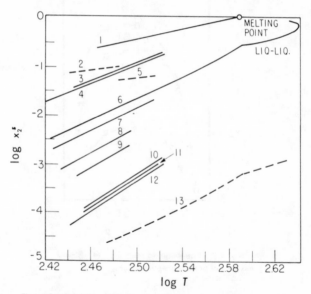

Fig. 4.8 Solubility of iodine in various solvents.
Solid lines denote violet "regular" solutions; dashed lines, yellow to brown solutions. (1) Ideal, (2) mesitylene, (3) bromoform, (4) carbon disulfide, (5) ethyl alcohol, (6) carbon tetrachloride, (7) n-heptane, (8) 1,1,2-trichloro-1,2,2-trifluoroethane, (9) dichlorohexafluorocyclobutane, (10) perfluorotributylamine, (11) perfluoromethylcyclohexane, (12) perfluoroheptane, (13) water.

variously colored yellow to brown. They contain complexes of iodine with the solvent and exhibit less disorder, less entropy, and smaller temperature dependence. These lines are not part of the regular solution family and require special treatment.

In Fig. 4.9 we see plotted, first the value of a_2^s, the activity of solid iodine, which is the solubility it would theoretically

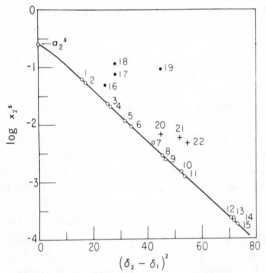

Fig. 4.9 Relation between the solubility of iodine in various solvents and the solubility parameters of solvent, δ_1, and iodine, 14.1.

(1) Bromoform, (2) carbon disulfide, (3) chloroform, (4) titanium tetrachloride, (5) carbon tetrachloride, (6) cyclohexane, (7) silicon tetrachloride, (8) 1,1,1-trichloro-2,2,2-trifluoroethane, (9) 1,1,2-trichloro-1,2,2-trifluoroethane, (10) 2,2,3-trichloroheptafluorobutane, (11) dichlorohexafluorocyclobutane, (12) perfluorotributylamine, (13) perfluoromethylcyclohexane, (14) a cyclic ether, c-$C_8F_{16}O$ (structure uncertain), (15) perfluoroheptane, (16) benzene, (17) p-dimethylbenzene, (18) mesitylene, (19) diethyl ether, (20) n-heptane, (21) isooctane, (22) 2-methylbutane.

have in a solvent with the same parameter as that of iodine, 14.1. The 15 open circles are for the solubility of iodine in 15 violet solutions. It is evident that they conform remarkably well to the equation.

The points 16, 17, 18 are for three aromatic solvents, benzene, *p*-xylene, and mesitylene. Their colors range from red to brown, indicating the presence of complexes. The solubility parameter of benzene is 9.2; if there were no complexing, the value of log x_2 would be close to that for the solution in chloroform, $\delta_1 = 9.0$. Complexing in ether, point 19, is exceedingly strong.

Points 20, 21, and 22 are for solutions in straight and branched flexible chain paraffins. These solutions are violet, hence the iodine is not complexed; the divergence is probably the effect of the far from compact shapes of the molecules of the solvents.

It should be noted that the theory of regular solutions succeeds in correlating solubilities of iodine in the violet solutions ranging from 5.58 mole per cent in CS_2 to 0.018 mole per cent in C_7F_{16}, a 300-fold range, and that kinetic theory is at the foundation of the theory of regular solutions.

To all readers who have stayed with the author to the end:

I thank you, and I congratulate you on your capacity to persist to the point of a not inconsiderable competence for thinking in terms of the powerful concepts of kinetic theory. The fact that this has been only an exploratory tour, and that mastery still lies far ahead, should not detract from a justifiable satisfaction in the insight you have already gained. You will find, I trust, that you can already answer with confidence most of the simpler, questions presented by natural phenomena or invented by professors like me. That should be fun; I hope you find it so. To each of you, good going, from here on!

INDEX

INDEX